QUOTIDIAN

Mary Wilkinson is a published writer of fiction, non-fiction and poetry. She has written for radio and is a Pushcart Prize nominee. She lives in Galway.

Quotidian

Mary Wilkinson

REFLEX PRESS

First published in 2023 by Reflex Press
Abingdon, Oxfordshire, OX14 3SY
www.reflex.press

A CIP catalogue record of this book is
available from the British Library.

ISBN: 978-1-914114-14-4

1 3 5 7 9 10 8 6 4 2

Cover image by Aleksandr Alekseev

www.reflex.press/quotidian/

For Will

'The beginning is always today.'

Mary Shelley

Begin

I am conflicted.

There are times

when the beginning

room appears of little value.

Yet, in the darkness

of night when

there is nothing

about to distract

I realise I

have to start

somewhere and that

is why a room,

any room,

even in its

seeming irrelevance

will suffice because

once entered

and dealt with

I can proceed,

confidently close

the door behind me

and walk down

the long passageway

of my mind

to where all

the other rooms

past and present

patiently await

my undivided attention.

Morning Light

Before all that happened there were times when I thought my dilemma was only my imagination. I confided in Miss C. Told her how frantic I was to keep the thoughts crowding into my mind at bay as the early morning light entered the bedroom of my young marriage. She knew too how good I was at putting those thoughts on hold as the day ever so kindly hesitated to allow me to temporarily settle back into the curve of his body. I was like a smooth shell back then, burrowed in warm sand waiting for the tide of daylight to dislodge and prod me gently from my resting place. When it did I only focussed on the morning chores and the children jostling over the small trinkets lodged at the bottom of the cereal box. Yet beneath the surface of these ordinary things, the doors to the rooms, tall, wooden and foreboding, somehow managed to loom before me. Yes, Miss C. knew too of the reality of those mornings when the man at my side stirred to fondle me and how I would not respond. She was aware too of how he could read the signs not to go any further as I rose into the chill room that offered little reprieve in the mid-winter of a place where the light, what precious little light there was, merely revealed itself as a pale, reluctant token.

Checklist

Bedrooms, bathrooms, living rooms, drawing rooms, dining rooms, attic rooms, waiting rooms, crying rooms, consulting rooms, dormitory rooms, hotel rooms, motel rooms, hospital rooms, junk rooms, confession rooms, recreation rooms, beauty rooms, operating rooms, meeting rooms, double rooms, single rooms, private rooms, public rooms, luxury rooms, basic rooms, clinic rooms, ballrooms, changing rooms, classrooms, cloakrooms, common rooms, darkrooms, family rooms, laundry rooms, tea rooms, green rooms, control rooms, funeral rooms, utility rooms, music rooms, hostel rooms, art rooms, red rooms, crap rooms, great rooms, lost rooms, find-yourself rooms, dying rooms, birthing rooms, thinking rooms, ceremony rooms, guessing game rooms, mindfulness rooms, what the hell are you doing rooms, where are you rooms, wishing rooms, longing for rooms, memory rooms, silent rooms, never forgetting you rooms, lovemaking rooms, crying in the doorway rooms, cold shoulder rooms, screaming rooms, door banging rooms, trying to understand rooms, bad news rooms, never getting anywhere rooms, trying again rooms, shut the fuck up rooms, goodbye rooms, closing the door rooms, turning the key rooms, walking away rooms, the ending of the beginning rooms. The beginning room.

Mother Time

For a while I am a young child again in my mother's kitchen. Me and, of course, Miss C. are standing on a chair that's pushed snugly up against the countertop. My task is to remove the skin from the almonds steeping in warm water. Mother is busy baking cakes. Winter time hosts clouds of condensation on the window panes of the steam-filled kitchen. Mother hums her little songs. My fingertips pucker like dried prunes. All that matters is here. All this activity keeps us bound together in aprons and tea towels and brown chipped baking bowls and weighing scales and orange peel and lemons and fruits and flours and parchment paper and white string, and always Mother humming away to herself with little songs about fairies and ferny mountains and strong men hunting by streams. I want her to stop and tell me something real. But the cakes and the songs rule. They are everything to her.

Once Mother took me to the city by train. The train carriage compartments had individual sliding doors and the curtains on the windows had red tasselled tiebacks. I wore brown leather shoes and a camel coat, and a woman on the train asked Mother if I was a coeliac, and Mother raging with her question, refused to respond and turned away to look out the window. I didn't know what that meant. Coeliac. I was only seven. The woman who asked if I was a coeliac gobbled down coloured jellies from a brown paper bag. She kept putting the colours into her mouth like her life depended on it, and I wanted just one bright green jelly to grace my lips. I watched her eat them one after the other, and she saw me watching her. I could tell she didn't like me watching her. My mother took a dot-to-dot book out of her bag, and I remember how easy it was to trace the paths, and when we got to the city we went to a tearoom for tea and there were plates of cakes in the middle of each table on gold tiered stands, and the woman in a little peaked hat served us tea in china cups covered in pink roses. When I asked my mother to pour some tea out for Miss C. as well, she called for an extra cup. I knew more than anyone how Miss C. loved those big curved windows wrapped around the street as much as I did and how, when my mother looked down at the street, we both could tell that she was hopeful someone familiar might appear and wave up at her. I had a slice of chocolate cake to eat with a red Smartie on top.

Biding Time

All those rooms needing to be explored; the beginning rooms and the proper-ending room, the rooms in the middle, and the not-so-obvious rooms and then the not-in-any-proper-order rooms because we all know there can be times when memory refuses to cooperate.

Sister

Now that I have started this process I see how the only rule I need to employ is the gradual unleashing of the accumulation of rooms plaguing my mind and how emptying those out will eventually clarify matters and explain the consequences to follow. You see, all those rooms played such a vital role in ensuring that the end turned out as it did. Please, I must repeat myself on that several times. I'm sure you understand enough to stay with me on this. It will prove fruitful. I promise.

I was twelve or thirteen years old. Does a year really matter at that age? It does at the time but now, of course not. I am sure that I must have been happy, stretched out on the bed in my room, looking up at a poster on the wall of a shiny pop star with frizzy hair and white teeth. Or I could very well have been wearing blue overalls and reading a DH Lawrence novel depending on my mood and fad. I might have been in love with a boy who passed me secret love letters across his boarding school wall. I might have had parents and a dog and a garden where mourning doves predictably cooed from strategic perches in the trees beside the river. I might even have had a sister who sometimes came to visit and brought me bundles of old Vogue magazines. She was older than me so I didn't know her too well. But she was my sister. She smelled of far-off cities and fragrant oils. I loved how she tossed her hair forward and brushed it like it was a separate part of her that she had to care for. In a memory, she shares a bed with me this night, and we are eating apples and looking at the magazines and we are talking in broken sentences like it doesn't really matter what we are saying to each other. It's a luxury though to be eating midnight apples. That is it. Now she is gone. Still alive but gone from me. I put that room somewhere safe because it is all I have of her. So go ahead and call it sour grapes on my part. Call it a hopeless case. Call it the way the atmosphere made an ending to a part of the story before any proper beginning even had a chance. This room is getting a small section of the entire building. It will be placed on the northern side exactly where the light will never penetrate. The blinds are to remain closed, and nobody will be allowed to enter without prior notice. So be advised to stay well away as there is nothing further to be discussed. Ever.

Ghosts

Pendulum sway, O pendulum sway, pendulum sway away. I am sixteen years old now and sitting beside Miss C. on the steps that lead upstairs. The clock in the hall says pendulum sway, at least that's what it says to me. I repeat the words over and over as I wait for Mother. I wait for Mother as the heavy brass heart moves back and forth, its constant rhythm tick-tocking the minutes away. A bell in the bowels of this house rings ceaselessly and soon after, the kettle on the stove sings its song. It's only Harry making tea. Again. Where's Mother gone to? Yesterday I heard her and Harry talking. He kept repeating words to her over and over like luscious, luscious, sexual, luscious, luscious, pendulum sway, sexual. Why won't Mother come? I need to tell her about my school skirt. Ask her if there's a chance I can get a new one. The tartan has so many shaggy bits of wool hanging off it, and no matter how often I pull at them, more grow back like weeds in the driveway. Harry makes it worse by teasing me and saying I look like an ugly crow in my black woolly tights. I'm wishing he were gone. I'm wishing I could stop the pendulum, wishing I could erase all those words and go back to the beginning. Why is the beginning always so much nicer than the ending?

Bedsit

There was a sink in the corner and a makeshift stove and a narrow bed on the other side, and not much else but a small chair and a rickety wardrobe. Ah yes. I can see it still with the big window that saved it by somehow opening up the room so that it appeared to extend out into the back gardens of the tall old houses on the other side that bordered the park. I liked to stand and watch the black cats steal along the uneven walls and the pigeons holding their town hall meetings in the afternoons. And there was the guy downstairs from Chicago who insisted I listen to his Paul Simon album. The guy downstairs from Chicago who always knocked on my door.

The beginning is therefore in this linoleum-floored room. Cold. Wake up and sit up and place your bare feet on the linoleum floor and walk across to put the kettle on. Pour water into basin, and with a washcloth squeezed tight, wash your face, then your underarms, then between your legs. Dress. Wear a brown corduroy dress the colour of autumn leaves. Midnight blue stockings. Eat something. A piece of bread. Stand by the window and look out. The sky is a broken blue promise decorated with grey piping. Wait for a moment and ask yourself where did it begin? Here. You lie to yourself. Here.

All the men meeting in the office liked their coffee served at ten a.m. When I brought it to them they kept on speaking and never looked up to thank me. Silver spoons sang on china.

Froth was spit on milky foam. Suits grey. Red ties with diamonds and gold cuff links. Initials everywhere. DMC's my boss. DMC dictated his mind, and I typed it down. Rattle, rattle on DMC barking at me, please can you run this over to RBC? Can you book dinner for six tonight at the GBC? That coffee was way too strong today for me. You'll need to; you'll need to dispense with your attitude. I'm warning you. Sorry, I'd say to DMC. I will. Carry on. Lunchtime.

The beginning was then. Mr DMC and his busyness and Miss C. and me his little busyness helper.

Apples and cheese in the park nearby, sitting on a bench of my own. Shiny grass blades like sharp silver knives gloating in sunlight. Shadows loomed through trees. Heads bent. Air.

Passing down through streets and cross over the pavements waiting and watching, listening to keep going. Where to? I did not know, but it helped to feel the motion. Stopping at the lights to listen for silence that never came.

Bookstore opened up. A sign read, please come in. So I pushed the fragile glass door to step quietly inside. Tiny bell. Bing. Ring. Spling. Silence. Silence of pages turning. Sweet pages. Smells of brown bread books and roses and sweat and pain and pleasure and sex and fears and memories and uncertain beginnings and for certain ends. Tall shelves made narrow streets. Ochre streets with books for shops and topsy-turvy houses. And I was lost. Nice lost though like I wanted to be lost strolling down the ochre street and allowing my hands to run along the bindings in expectation. Stop. A hand on my shoulder. You. He said. You. And he was old. Older. He was saying will you? Would you? Want to? Please. Me. And I asked, are you talking to me? You, he said, yes, you. Might I said. Might. Go on, he said. His books in his hands. His hands a painting. Fingers draped around his books. His bony fingers holding his books. Please, he whispered. Maybe. I might. I'll see, I said.

Night. Boil the kettle. Wash the face. Underarms. Between the legs. Stand by window. The Yank outside the door calling my name. Nothing said, just me looking at the tall walls for cats. None to be seen. Me listening for his steps to die away on the stairs. Waiting. Wishing for the beginning to happen. Wondering when.

He came calling at nine and sat on the narrow bed looking out the window. He liked the window. It's interesting, he said. He crossed his legs and hunched forward to rest his long thin hands like precious gifts on his thighs. Black veins ran into streams at his wrists. I watched him looking out and at me, and then he shifted his body to make room for me and patted the bed. I crossed over while he looked at me with eyes blue like asters in a jade pot. I was reddening myself. You are, he said, beautiful, and he reached into his pocket to take out a small pewter box. This is your beginning box, he said. Cold pewter box with a pewter frog on top, and it was the first beginning gift I remember. He stroked his beard and kept looking at me. What then? Make tea. Yes. Cold linoleum needed tea. So older man who brought me pewter with pewter frog as a beginning box took off his coat, and I made him tea.

There were mornings when I did not want to look out the window. Mornings when I tried to remember where I began and why I forgot. If I lay on the bed at a certain angle, I could only see sky. Everything else was omitted. It was then that I felt safe because the sky was there, big and strong to save me from all that was unwelcome. I could look up and not see anybody. Older man disappeared and Mr DMC disappeared and the guy from downstairs from Chicago who loved Paul Simon disappeared until all I had was the sky looking down at me and Miss C. beside me urging me to begin.

What happened then is that the older man with the pewter box came calling every night with presents of poems and shells and sometimes sticky flaky buns from the posh bakery on the posh street. He'd watch me eat them and laughingly ask, where did I get you at all? And when he brought me enough poems and shells and sticky flaky buns, he began to take off my clothes, and I lay naked on the bed until he carefully covered me with the scratchy blanket before lying down beside me, always watching me like he was afraid I would disappear. Sad older man with his wistful, what-if face that never left him once he started to talk about his life. Each chapter was small with only a few pages. There was nothing remarkable about it. When the window darkened and the cats slept, he asked me to hold it. His dick. He said, hold my dick. I hesitated to touch it, but he persisted, so I held his hot wood in my hands. Pulsing wood that wanted me. Do you like it, he said. Yes. Maybe. I. Will we, he asked? Will we, you know? Yes. I wanted it. He laid me back down, and his face hovered over mine. I felt him spread my legs and then push in. Slowly, take it slowly, older man. Take it easy. There he said, isn't it nice. Maybe, I say. Maybe it is.

I never saw the older man after that. He might have died in a grey room somewhere full of shells and unread poems. Or maybe, just maybe, all he ever wanted was to do what he did to me that one time. Whatever. I gathered up the shells and the poems he gave me, and I threw them out of the window. They drifted sadly down into the brambles below. The pewter box I left on the windowsill where it tarnished over time to eventually become something it never promised to be in the first place.

First Love

I lay in a room not far from the sea where the seals in the harbour were to be heard barking incessantly, and the foghorn sounding all night long was enough to soothe me through many sleepless hours. Everything was special about being in this room. Even now I can still smell the promise of good coffee coming from down the hall. I want to go towards it, but something stops me. It must only be a ghost rattling cups and saucers about, tapping the spoons as if in beat to an old tune.

The bay window faced the sea, and the acacia trees beyond in the neighbouring yard arched together to form a perfect, natural frame. He was forever talking about the allergies brought on by the acacia trees. I never heard the like of it. And poison ivy in the undergrowth too. Everything was a potential threat. But the presence of the sea saved me. It was the salve required. Even when he turned sour and stopped bringing me scrambled eggs in bed with just picked parsley scattered on top. Morning dew drops nestling in the leaves were silver pearls. Hot, nutty coffee served in tiny blue cups. I remember how he'd place the tray down on the old oak floorboards and climb back into bed until we turned into out of control people looking for something that wasn't possible. Oh the pleasure, the raw sex that had me forget about everything else. Temporarily. That's it, he'd say, you can do it and drew back to look down at me and turned away and rose and dressed and walked out and returned the next day and started all over. Ah, but that glorious bevelled glass can distort the view, and the wooden win-

24

dow frames began to rot in the damp sea air. One day I looked out to see how the bark of the acacia trees had turned gnarly and rough. I begged him to come and see. But all he said in reply was, that's how it goes. You should know, he said. And he was right. I knew. I know now too. I do tend to wonder though if he ever replaced the window frames and if his neighbours agreed to have the acacia trees chopped down. If they had, there would have been no reason whatsoever to go into that room because all that was outside the room made that room. It was the only reason for being there in the first place.

The Confident Rooms

Have you ever gone walking in the city once darkness falls in? I mean to say, walking without any purpose in mind but just to walk for the fun of it? I used to do that. At any opportunity I'd quickly don the long black coat that I bought in a charity shop, pull on my fleece boots and walk through the suburban neighbourhoods just as people had arrived home from a long day of work and were beginning to prepare their evening meal, or light a fire or put the kettle, soothed by the comforting hiss of gas from the stove. All of those wondrous rooms where people switched on the lights, eased off their shoes and opened up newspapers. I was once struck by the beauty of a slender woman as she stood beside a vintage lamp turning the pages of a book. I immediately recalled a painting I had seen somewhere. And on most of my outings I saw how the tired parents of young children hovered over their equally tired offspring, who constantly fidgeting at kitchen tables, struggled over homework. And how is it that the sight of a single crystal glass of ruby wine, placed on a dark mahogany sideboard, alongside an open book filled me with such an intense sense of pleasure and longing? I'll admit that on those lone excursions I saw hundreds of T.V. screen lights flickering eerily with a welcoming light, like blue sunshine on the faces of old men dozing on ragged couches or onto the couples, observed through basement windows, who sat timidly side by side on single beds, the women bent over, graceful in the undoing of the laces of their tight shoes. And often I saw the seemingly necessary and permanent placement of a hostile house cat majestically perched on a wide window sill, swishing a long and bushy tail, while she looked out at the street and at me looking back in at her.

Miss C. was solely privy to my affection for the unoccupied rooms as they waited in their still, composed and almost confident presentation. Yes, the rooms never failed to appear confident to me in how they adopted a dignified stance in anticipation of the occupiers' return, knowing it was only a matter of time before they, the rooms, became vital and functional and essential once again to the householders' hustle and bustle. Yes, no doubt the rooms emitted that trusting sense of expectation for the owners to come inside and with a great rush of activity go to switch on the lamps and light some candles whilst remarking out loud and not to any one in particular, as they casually tossed their overcoats onto the coat rack in the hallway, 'Oh, it's so good to be home. I actually never realised, until this very minute, how much I love these rooms.'

Honeymoon

What about the Rock-a-Bye Motel? Not too far from the Four Corners. Stuck in the middle of nowhere. I know. Don't laugh. Although it is ironic. Four Corners with not a wall to be seen for hundreds of miles. Honeymoon. Just married. Unconventional wedding. Small gathering. Four people. Two witnesses. A woman who was a minister of something or other to bind the knot. A stray friend. Me barefoot in a cotton dress. Three bottles of champagne to pop. Life beckoned. And that motel room. Room 122 with its vibrating bed and erratic shower and view of the diner across the street, and fried Indian bread for breakfast with honey and pats of butter and bitter, bitter coffee that tasted so impossibly good before the sun came up burning strong as the days progressed. I can see him now stretched out on the bed, long smooth tanned torso, his big, glorious feet spread wide. I am coming out of the bathroom wrapped in a towel, and he's saying to me, 'Come here, my brand new wife, come to me,' and I did. I came to him with my long wet hair tumbling out of the towel down onto his skin to make goose bumps in the midday heat, and he kissed me everywhere. Lovemaking in the Rock-a-Bye Motel. Room 122. Bed bugs optional.

Ice Shavings

Writing once more about my mother is of a time when the rooms we once occupied together change course. This time the kitchen countertop and the teashop become a bed beside a window in a hospital room. My mother lies on the bed dying, but she doesn't know that. July is on the wane. I have a son. I can see him outside kicking a ball on a small patch of grass near the parking lot. He's talking to himself like he's a commentator at a soccer game. The room angry with illness does not relent, even when I open the window. The fruit salad I made for my mother sits in a plastic bowl. Untouched. Apples and strawberries grieve for air. Beyond this room life carries on as normal. A lawnmower roars in the distance. Car horns blare. An ice cream truck tempts with a light and cheery melody, reminiscent of happier times. My mother puts her hand out to touch me. Her hands are still beautiful, and if they could speak they would surely say, 'Look at me. I did ok. Didn't I? Are you alright now? Everything will work out. Bends in the road and all that carry on. There's always a bend in the road, and there's always a tomorrow and a new beginning.' No, there's not. No more beginnings for my mother. Out with that now. I hold her hand. It has no strength. It rests like a fallen leaf in my palm. Soon it will crumble into nothingness, and I will be here eventually writing this down. Mother. Son with ball on lawn. His brown limbs akimbo. Warm water in a plastic bottle. Straws. Sips. Ice shavings on lips. Room full of sadness.

There will be a train journey home. I will say goodbye, Mother. I will call a taxi and cry all the way to the train station with my son sitting beside me. I will buy him a jigsaw puzzle to distract. I will sit by the window on the train and see you, Mother, waving in at me. You are framed in fuchsia with a bundle of wild mint firmly clasped in your hands, and you just wrapped a loaf of brown bread in a towel and put it on the windowsill to cool. You are singing again, always singing your silly songs without reason. Forgotten words, but the tune and the urge to sing never failed. The train window gives you back to me. Briefly, the big T.V. screen of a train window reflects your life as it flashes by, and I am seeing you as if you are concentrated into a small black and white home movie. You never saw the dark shadow coming, did you? It lurked in the sidelines knowing that all the days were only gathering momentum, patiently waiting for this day to appear and to put the final curtain into place.

But Can You See Miss C.?

I need to figure something out, something I have long deliberated in my mind, so by putting it down here once and for all on the page, matters might or should be clarified. You see, I am trying to remember how and where the madness began. Was it when my father told me to go back upstairs and take the dress off that my sister had sent to me in a brown paper package all the way from London because he was worried what people would think, or was it before that, when at around age five, I asked my mother to please leave the door open for Miss C. because she hadn't yet come into the room and surely, surely my mother knew that it was rude to shut the door in somebody's face. But my mother said, 'Where is your friend?' and I said, 'Mother, can't you see her, look right behind me, Mother,' and I pointed to Miss C. who stood perfectly poised and still waiting by the door, and I said, 'She is so happy to be here, Mother, and to have you as her mother too, aren't you Miss C.?

Eleven A.M.

I know I haven't said much about happiness. Even if regret-fully it is only a brief, fleeting emotion, it still needs to be dis-cussed with nothing short of reverence. It is true that I was never very practical, nor was I one to go overboard on any un-realistic expectations of happiness either. So just imagine be-ing in this room. Can you see it? Yes, the carpet is a blend of turquoise and jade green. How did you know that it reminds me of a September seascape? The walls are a sepia shade like kelp strewn on the shore. One small armchair is neatly placed beside the tall window. I often times remarked to Miss C. as to where would we be in this life without windows, especially the big, soft, open trusting windows. I believe windows to be the eyes of a room. It's true. I'm telling you, eyes.

Sitting on a chair in this room I am naked apart from my dainty black velvet slippers. My dark lustrous hair tumbles forward to form a sheath of sorts across my breasts. My pure white body is almost translucent so that it catches the evening light and appears to shine right through me to reveal my ribcage like an abacus ready to be counted. If you look closely enough you will notice how my hands are lightly grasped be-fore me as if I am trying to come to terms with some type of a predicament, or maybe it is nothing more than that I am wait-ing for somebody to call. Am I happy in this room? Possibly, briefly, yes. I don't know yet. This day I rise and pace and dis-tractedly pour myself a glass of clear liquid. I put the glass down on the table by the lamp and pick up a book of words that matter, but still I walk around the room like somebody lost in a dream. It is clear now that I am waiting for my lover who is late. Happiness is deferred. So I go to lie on the bed and spread myself out to reach down into the place of pleasure with Miss C. watching me from the shadows. I easily find the core to bring the orgasm to open me up. To. Myself. There. I come. Sated I rise to stand in the centre of the room where yellow and blue flowers appear at my feet, magically sprouting from between my toes. I throw my head back and picture the beginning of night. It is like the end of coming when the darkness in your eyes gives way, and you begin to see the light appearing out of it. Like the way a sudden shaft of light creates a sense of relief while at the same time it reveals the silvery threads of the cobwebs dancing on the ceiling where a tiny spider busily scurries along. It crosses my mind how the journey is so long and arduous for such a tiny creature to endure. All those miles and miles that make up the wide expanse of ceiling space, where the ornate coils on the plasterwork become an alien terrain needing to be traversed and then on down the smooth stretch of white walls that eventually collide into a corner, where tiny spider, thinking he has finally arrived at his destination, feels extremely pleased with himself for having survived. It is a shame, and I am sorry to admit this, but I have no choice but to raise the heel of my foot and replace it ever so quickly down onto silly old spider as he dares to pass before me. Yes, I have to say light reveals so much happiness before darkness falls.

A Windowless Square with a Filing Cabinet, a Desk, a Lamp, a Chair and a Waste Basket

His office was a windowless square with a filing cabinet, a desk, a lamp, a chair and a waste basket. When once I asked him how he could possibly survive in a room without a window, he seemed completely taken aback by my question, as if he never considered it, before he resumed the task of correcting his students' papers, only pausing now and then to sip from his coffee cup. I persisted though, and to goad him into answering, I remarked how even prison cells have windows. He didn't seem to hear that. I decided not to repeat myself although looking back on it now, I believe he did hear me and did not know how to respond. If he said he didn't care about a window, it would have looked bad, and if he said it really bothered him that he didn't have a window, it would have looked bad because it would appear as if he were complaining, and he certainly wasn't about to do that, being the brand new professor fresh off the internship salary, full of gusto to reveal what was stored away in his head in the twelve years it took him to get there. He wasn't about to make waves. All that mattered to him was wanting more than anything to be popular with faculty and students alike. Keeping that purpose in mind he rose each day at dawn, breakfasted on cereal and coffee and drove to the campus, where he walked with a confident and purposeful stride to his windowless office.

In the beginning I tried to fix up his windowless office. I bought him a green ferny plant to put on his desk. Even though the florist assured me it was an ideal choice for a windowless office, the plant quickly turned brown until it shriv-elled into a mini brittle skeleton that he threw in the waste basket. Shortly after that I hung a colourful poster of a seaside resort in the south of France up on the windowless wall. The view, seen through a tall window with white shutters, opened out into a lemon grove with the azure sea in the background dotted with dozens of white sailboats. On the golden beach, parasols flapped to shade tanned bodies lingering in a trance-like state by the edge of the sea. But only after a couple of days he admitted that he had taken the poster down, believing it to be inappropriate, that it clashed with his research and the se-rious mood of the room. After that I left his office the way it was, a windowless square with a filing cabinet, a desk, a lamp, a chair and a waste basket. And each day, I went about my business focused solely on domestic matters such as finding the best scouring pads or searching out the deals and specials the stores had to offer or if I could buy some avocados at the market, what recipe would I use for them? That kind of thing. I never once during this time realised my mind was becom-ing a windowless room too, despite Miss C. pulling me aside to assure me of my demise. Now what I say might be irrelevant, but looking back I see that I never once considered putting a plant in my mind room. Something vibrant with fertile soil is what my mind room would have benefited from. I never tried to doctor it up. I never tried to go out shopping for words to hang around in my mind. I'm thinking of the millions of exotic words I could have strung together like interesting beads that would have complimented the one before and the one right af-ter. Things that I might have wanted to do. Might have imag-ined. But instead;

I was cleaning the toilet.

I was hanging out the clothes.

I was washing the floor.

I was wiping up the mess on the table.

I was potty training.

I was pacing around rooms, wondering what was wrong with them.

I was fixing up the rooms outside of me.

I was looking out.

I was ignoring my room.

I was painting the walls.

I was fixing the locks.

I was scrubbing the pots.

I was emptying the dishwasher.

I was stocking the larder.

I was recycling the trash.

I was loading the washing machine.

I was contemplating detergents.

I was negotiating traffic.

I was wiping away tears.

I was rummaging through a tin box looking for band-aids.

I was choosing new carpets.

I was washing the windows.

I was making the casseroles.

I was baking the cookies.

I was watching out for him.

I was ironing his shirts.

I was picking out his ties.

I was gasping for air.

I was trying to find the window.

I was trying to ask if a window could be installed.

I was gagging for air.

I was on the floor.

I was getting up.

I was saying nothing.

I had forgotten what to say.

I never remembered again.

When all is said and done, it seems you can easily become accustomed to windowless rooms. After a while you even tend to forget what a window looks like. Why, even the tiniest window becomes irrelevant.

The Kiss

In a beige tract house that shadowed a desert, I became a proper housewife. Proper and solitary I politely existed in air-conditioned rooms, religiously scrutinizing the walls for the scorpions who stalked me and baby when they emerged from the alien landscape of the grey air vents. Try to picture me back then as I tied brightly coloured bandanas in my hair and bought bags of avocados and warm tortillas and bottles of tequila where solitary worms floated like bobbing astronauts lost in space. And I cannot but mention those cloudless skies stretching into infinity and so blue except at sunset that is when random streaks of orange might appear as if to compensate for the monotony. Why, come to think of it, even the night sky eventually turned midnight blue with token golden stars that could fool me into thinking they were beautiful.

But what of the rooms, you might ask. Well, the rooms by the desert were all the same. Square, convenient and cool, these rooms were equally distributed so you could hear any doorbell that chimed or screen door that slammed. I had a waste disposal unit that belched and often became clogged with corn husks and apple cores and coffee grinds, and in the spacious en suites off the well-proportioned bedrooms, white tiles gleamed alongside silent power showers. The his-and-her sinks hosted his-and-her towels perfectly folded on ceramic towel rails, and tucked away in the utility room my huge washing machine churned and whirled alongside my bigger clothes dryer, diligently drying the clothes in the dark, stagnant privacy of the remote-controlled garage, while out on the sidewalk a cheeky red and blue mailbox gaped in fear at the endless sandstorms that blew in from the desert to descend on the glass windows of those rooms and, dare I say, on the glass windows of Mr Bernstein's rooms down the street. Mr Bernstein, you say. Yes. I met him early one morning before the sun got too high. I simply stopped to pass the time of day with him. He was out sweeping his driveway. He was old. So old that his knobbly knees pushed out through the paper-thin skin of his legs. He wore khaki shorts and a big-rimmed sun-hat, and he looked up at me as I walked by with Miss C., who lagged behind, complaining as usual. It is only now that I think it funny how Husband was never interested in hearing any-thing I had to say about Mr Bernstein. All he cared about was teaching his protégés at the university and grading papers, committee meetings and research.

Mr Bernstein was, what can I say, gallant, I suppose, in an old fashioned, wrinkly, predictable, granddad kind of way, and there was no reason whatsoever why we were not to quickly become friends. It was easy. After all we might as well have been two stray desert rats. We talked almost every other day because, as I said, before the sun got too high he was to be found out on his driveway bringing in the trash cans or weed-ing the pebbly patch that made up his small cacti garden. Then, one day Mr Bernstein called by the house, and I let him in, and we chit-chatted while baby napped. The house was perfectly tidy and still, and it felt so normal to be enter-taining Mr Bernstein in the living room. He appeared to be younger on that particular day, calmly sitting in the cool liv-ing room in his freshly ironed Hawaiian shirt, his thinning hair smoothed down close to his head. Then before I could even consider what was happening, he began to visit every day but only always for thirty minutes, sitting on the couch with the untouched glass of sun tea I'd poured out for him as he spoke nostalgically about New York and how he had only come to the desert hoping it would help him with his arthritis. No, he never married, never met anyone that special, he said, winking at me. And then one morning he arrived with a black orchid wrapped in shiny wrapping paper, and in the small suburban room, Mr Bernstein placed his dry lips onto mine and said everything without saying a word. Then we sat across from one another and made small talk, and I waited for the thirty minutes to end until eventually he rose and shuffled out into the midday glare. His familiar shadow appeared two days later. I could see him through the tinted glass in the porch door, patting down his freshly laundered shirt before pressing his finger to the ding dong doorbell that was to go unanswered. Instead I turned and walked back into the air-conditioned living room to sit myself down on the couch and wait for my mind to quieten and for the room to revert back into another neat and ordinary beige square in the middle of a brown rectangle-shaped housing estate, perched on the edge of the never-ending desert and the permanently blue sky.

Breasts

Bodies and beauty and lust and the endless quest for perfectly shaped breasts and bottoms and arms and hands and lips and feet and faces and chins and will you or won't you and love you and hate you and nothing and everything and flowers that have never felt sunlight delivered to maternity wards and on birthdays, and what about those little yellow post it notes stuck on the refrigerator door with silly hearts drawn on them, and the holding of hands at night walking along a darkening street, and then both of you listening for the kids to come home in the early hours of the morning, and he sometimes bringing you coffee in bed and he knowing what you are going to say before you know what you are going to say, and then all the happiness forgotten about as it disappears into the walls of the breast-clinic rooms alongside other women gathered together into a waiting room where a bright oversized T.V. screen tells you that it is Christmas and everything on it appears nostalgic yet too shiny at the same time. And then there's a woman on the television screen with the much sought-after body, and I can tell that she's wearing a well-fitting bra underneath her perfect white silk blouse while she shares with us her perfect skincare routine and her perfect life and how she manages to always make the perfect cakes for the perfect holiday. And we, the unwilling audience, wait with our breasts, reminding ourselves not to even think about relaxing as we sit upright and alert in our backless paper gowns for Mr Breast Man to call us in. He will tell us if we are to have a happy Christmas or not. And when I am summoned I glance back at the other women who nod at me in solidarity as if to say go on, go on, you'll be fine. You're a woman, for God's sakes. I go then to lie down on the consulting room table wearing a gown the colour of a pale dawn sky in June. The nurse pulls a moss-green curtain around me. I am waiting with my heart that's like a hyperactive drum sequestered in an otherwise still room until he swishes in like an icy draught through the heavy door. Clean and cool this Mr Breast Man. I want to say, You are so beautiful, Mr Breast Man. Did you remember to kiss your wife this morning before you came to this examination room to trawl my breasts? Your hands are silken as they probe for alien beings. Tell me, are we not all the same to you now? Simply faceless women clad in paper gowns the colour of dawn skies in June, hoping they can soon go home to bake mince pies and wrap gifts? Are some women going to be told they cannot go home today? Is that day waiting for all of us? Mr Breast Man, can we all go home today? Is there any point in us staying? I like your eyes, Mr Breast Man. Your eyes are like deep grey lakes with bulrushes for eyelashes, upright and resilient despite a strong wind. I like the way we are here together in this white, fluorescent room with only the sound of women walking down the corridor. The sound they make is a gentle sound like feet shod in fleece and as soft as a newborn baby's fontanel lightly dusted in mellow prayer chants that hail from a place miles and miles from here.

Renovation

Once upon a long time ago, after we had returned to this green place far from the arid land, we had a dividing wall removed so it was possible for us to roam freely from one room to the next without having to walk down the long draughty hallway. The builder came to knock down the wall, and the first words to come out of his mouth were, 'I'll take two sugars and a drop of milk'. Eventually after he'd smoked a few cigarettes and finished slurping his tea, he heaved a sledgehammer into the air and started to furiously tear away at the plaster. Big chunks and tiny sneaky clever pieces flew off, and dust went everywhere, covering the bookcase and the mantelpiece, and it scurried like frightened mice up onto the dresser, where it settled permanently on the bric-a-brac on the shelves. But the builder kept going until the desired effect was achieved. When he was done he tossed his hammer on top of the pile of plaster on the floor and said that he'd return the next day to clean up. After he left we went back and forth through that gap like children who discovered a new game to play. Delighted with ourselves, we were. Miss C. was just as ecstatic as me, believing we had finally unearthed a new sense of freedom, a fresh start with me on one side and with him on the other side waving delightedly, laughing at our own silliness. That day it was as if we had broken something invisible inside of us just by knocking down that wall, and we both agreed the arch really brought new life into the rooms. But now I know differently. I know now we were only playing a silly game because, to be honest, moving rooms about isn't always a good idea. For one you can never properly rid the residue no matter how often you try to dust and clean up, and really I came to realise that keeping four walls in a room is essential to making a room a proper room because walls are the skin that you need to have to hold the core together. Yes, I distinctly recall confiding in Miss C. about how walls bind the skeleton of what otherwise could collapse into nothing or, at the very least into something resembling a terrible finality.

Girl Talk

Who would have guessed that I was a lonely being back then? That is apart from Miss C., of course. She knew everything about me. But even if anybody happened to be aware of my predicament they would most likely have said that I brought it all upon myself. Insisted that it is just what I deserved for thinking I was better off than the rest of them. They would definitely have said, who does she think she is anyway with her highfalutin ways, rarely agreeable to play along with the game, the pretence of something where you had to follow the rules no matter what, but oh no, not her, no, all she was on about was only wanting to get to the bottom of everything, to toss back the curtains, to look beneath the carpet, to dig up the dirt. What was the point in all of that? So they agreed to best leave her to her own resources and to rot in the mire.

Oh, but it wasn't all lonely. There were times, albeit in the early days, when I surely would have laughed at someone asking me if I was lonely. There wasn't any reason to be lonely. There were days that were never long enough. All those demands on me, but I kept going. Spinning around I was. Yes, me. You know, wait. Did you know that you can be in a room full of people and still feel lonely? I admit I've been there. You stand in the corner and survey the scene, searching and hoping to find yourself mirrored in somebody else, trying to connect, and guess what, you can't find anything or anyone, so you end up stranded in your own fucked up loneliness. Miss C. always encouraged my bad language. I know how unneces-sary it is to use these horrible expletives but, but at the same time totally understandable. Yes? What happens then? Well, you might find you start drinking too much to cover up the awkwardness, all the while nodding your head, listening to women talk the girl talk about the latest high heels, handbags, the way the husbands bother the shit out of them, how maybe they'll dye their eyebrows, employ a detox routine and get a bit of botox around the eyes and sure while they're at it why not tackle the thinning lips as well. And then all of them laughing and drinking back a little more. Not too much, mind girls, mind, careful, now. We all know how the mantra goes; a moment on the lips, a lifetime on the hips.

Sleepless

A dead end. That's what I whispered to Miss C. back then. That I was headed down a dead-end street where all the rooms folded in on themselves and made it appear impossible for me to join them together anymore, to make a nice house from them, and so I often found myself thinking I should get out and move on and try and make a go of something else, but that was easier said than done. And really, face it, it was getting a little late in the day, a small bit long in the tooth, the over and over again of what I should have or have not done.

It was at night around that time when I would lie in bed like a stone, frightened and asking myself how I got to be this way. Were there ever nights when my pillow welcomed sleep? There must have been. Those nights when I confidently lay my head down and closed my eyes to allow the lull of promised dreams to lure me away from the room in which I slept. Those nights when nothing was present until I woke the following morning renewed and happy. How I was ready for the world then, the day ahead, getting up and stretching myself out and going downstairs to make the coffee. But what happened? Did I get tired of it? Of the whole damn humdrum of routine? But that has to be considered a sin. Is it not? Should I have simply decided to embrace the floor beneath my feet? Be glad I had a floor to stand on?

And I certainly wasn't oblivious to how Miss C. looked at me and made no attempt to disguise her scorn at the sag of skin.

It's called wrinkling. Definition: the preparation of the body for the end. All the magic creams in that fancy department store won't change that. No matter how much salve I rub on my skin. No matter how many times I tuck in my tummy. No matter how much healthy food I try to eat. No matter how many long walks I take. What did you say? Did he still want me after all I'm revealing here? Sometimes. Did I enjoy it? Sometimes. Did I ever enjoy it? Yes. Of course I did. Yes. Sometimes.

Frame

The window is a frame with me standing in the middle so I decide to put the frame on the wall and the frame on the wall faces the flowered June garden where I spend my time looking out at the flowered June garden wishing the flowered June garden could look like this all the time with its pink and purple and yellow canvas when I sense someone standing behind me and I turn to see him in the frame of the doorway and he fills the doorway well with his frame, he asks me, what are you doing in that frame, are you okay, you look so thoughtful and I say I'm alright, I am just a woman in a frame looking out at a flowering garden in June thinking about nothing in particular, turning around to see a man in the frame of a doorway and thinking how he fills the frame so well and with that he comes from his frame to join me in mine, and I have to move over a little to allow him in, and he kisses the back of my neck before he too stands still looking out at the flowered June garden, and then I wonder what does this frame look like from the garden with the man and the woman looking out at a flowered garden in June until I begin to realise that I could, if I really wanted to, count the number of Junes left before the ending is reached, before the frame becomes redundant to be placed on a shelf and occasionally dusted by someone who will glance at it before putting it back down again.

Broken

I had to remind Miss C. how my rooms were prone to disappearing without any warning whatsoever. Yes, it's true; I can speak from experience here how rooms can elude and confuse as quickly as they can appear to make sense. One day it is possible to discover that you are not in any room that has one meaningful attachment to it. It is possible that, seemingly overnight, without any prior consultations, the rooms have weirdly decided to morph into one giant cavernous place that cannot be readily identified. For a minute or two you might think you are still asleep coming towards the final scene of a dream, but no, that is not the case because you are fully awake, although it seems the kitchen and the dining room and the bedroom and the waiting rooms and the bathrooms have all knitted together into one massive room and there are no single, distinctive sounds coming from these rooms but a bunch of garbled echoes all at once combined as if they are being broadcast through a loud speaker and down a great dark long tunnel. They're repeating sentences that don't add up:

Pray tell me, dear, but what day of the week is it?

Where's my sweet girl today?

Give Daddy a big kiss.

Upsy daisy.

Open your shirt.

Who is the president of the United States?

What's on T.V., Babba?

I hate you.

What's that stain on the floor all about?

Jesus cares.

Where are you from?

Save the whales.

Cut the crap.

Freedom for all.

What about the refugees?

Darling, let me touch you there now.

Stop.

What happened to the sunlight?

Save yourself first.

Sucker.

Mommy, I'm scared.

Stop that.

Touch me like this?

Bitch.

Hush.

I fell down.

I had a pain in my head.

I'm sorry.

What?

I'm sorry, Mommy.

Shhh,shhh,shhh,shhh,shhh,shhh.

No escape. No place to find peace. Only loud banging and clangs of pots and pans and china breaking up against steel doors slamming open and shut in my head that block me out of the rooms and gaping mouths opening and closing, saying nothing close to making any sense. And more racket. And me, begging Miss C. to save me from the hungry mouth of the steel cylinder, smooth and curved as an adobe church in New Mexico that opens up to swallow me into its bowel. Jesus. Where is this? Hell fills my ears. I can't breathe. I cannot breathe. I will die.

Then silence. The craved peace eventually comes, and there is only the svelte swish, swish of a wheelchair moving down a hospital corridor. And I'm remembering a long stretch of evening cycling my bicycle down to the shop to buy a chocolate bar. Daddy's treat. A ribbon of silver wrapping paper unravelling out behind me. Summer. The warm air on my skin. Bare feet free in open-toed sandals. A chocolate square stuck to my tongue. Close my eyes trusting the flight. It goes then, this reverie, as quickly as it came, just as I catch a glimpse of the girl riding away into a blood-orange sky. I never understood why she didn't look back when I called out her name. Not even for a sneaky glance.

Omission

I asked myself many times as to where the mad room happened to fit in all of this. I quietly pondered where in this story did the mad room fit and how come the mad room is blatantly omitted even though it reared its angry head to eventually play a major role? Even Miss C. was inclined to think it odd that I never once considered inclusion of the mad room on the long list I'd constructed and included earlier on in this account. How come it never crossed my mind? Or did it, and I conveniently yet subconsciously left it out? Surely it could have fit neatly right into the space between the junk room and the recreation room or in a perfectly appropriate spot preceding the crying room. How come I only mentioned it occasionally? As in, what about the mad room, before I took off again on a tangent leaving only a hint of its existence as if the mad room was some kind of a subliminal message that was not to go unnoticed but not to be so glaringly obvious either. Clever me. Although now that I come to own up to it, the mad room was a little more constant than I cared to accept at the time. Now I see how it was to be perfectly timed to go with the situation at hand. How whenever I went off on a little detail, he'd say to me, now remember there is always the mad room if you want to go there and then he would soften the effect by laughing it off straight away and pouring out a little more wine, predictably remarking on how especially good my pasta sauce tasted that night, and then we would carry on as if the mad room never did nor would exist. That's nonsense because now I know he was testing me, confidently aware that the fog-shrouded room of the future, after all the previous rooms were finally closed off, was what made the mad room an inevitability. It was to be only a matter of time.

Eavesdropping

Admittedly there were days when I wondered about my room obsession and how, in the end, all that talk might have been worthless. But then I realised that surely everyone, even secretly, must have been thinking of rooms as I had. Surely it was quite acceptable to pause and wistfully remark, 'Ah yes, I remember that room.' And that's easily explained because, in a strange way, the rooms carry us along life's pathway. Whether you like it or not, the rooms are permanently wedged in your brain and in your soul. The rooms perpetuate. Therefore, we unwittingly carry memories because of those very rooms. Dozens of rooms eagerly line up, waiting for us to re-enter them, each one determined to give us some definition, some reason for our existence.

There were many times when I stood outside a closed door, attempting to eavesdrop and peep through the keyhole. But I was rarely successful, being so conscious of the noise I made with my big bare feet sticking to the floor, or my body as my stomach growled or simply that my very existence was way noisier, more clumsy than the existences of other people. So I eavesdropped poorly by hearing nothing, or I might have heard murmurs of a sentence or two that made absolutely no sense at all, and if I dared to peep through the keyhole, I merely saw shapeless forms of human bodies crouching or sitting, and so, most of the time, I did not know if I was looking at a man or a woman. One time I thought I saw two women kiss intimately, but then the light changed in the room, enabling me to see more clearly, and I realised I was only imagining things, and in reality the supposed figures were only a shawl thrown across a mirror. I don't eavesdrop anymore, or for that matter, peep. One reason being that there is no one on whom to eavesdrop or peep, but the other reason being that even if there was someone on whom to eavesdrop or peep, I would not be bothered to eavesdrop or peep. I simply don't care to eavesdrop or peep anymore. And so I pass from room to room without pausing for very long. Once I have done the initial visit, well then, it is logical that I become a caretaker of sorts because rooms do require caretaking and a small bit of vigilance to ensure that they remain intact to exist in the original shape they aspired to be, as in, when I made them all those years before. Overall it is an easy task to undertake. Although it is wise that you always carry an itinerary with you. A well-considered checklist is an excellent aid for the various challenges or obstructions, or missing items that might prevent you from entering a room. There can be times when you might hesitate before actually turning the key, but it is then that a decision has to be made to keep the purpose foremost in your mind, and that is to not allow any fear to prevail and prevent that purpose and that purpose is to make sure all is in proper working order.[1]

---

1. Note: Rooms should never be allowed to fall into decay.

King Size, Balcony, Flat Screen, Walk-In Shower, Evening Turndown

I happen to be in a king-size hotel room with a tidy balcony overlooking the harbour where I can comfortably sit and watch the white-sailed boats being navigated by blonde-haired people clad in white shorts and white plimsolls and navy tee shirts, who wear three hundred dollar sunglasses, all the while patting the essential golden retriever. Note the chilled bottles of chardonnay on hand alongside the fat juicy olives stuffed with caviar, just in case. Even here in this king-size hotel room, the small refrigerator purrs invitingly to remind me of its well-stocked supply of blue vodka vials. There is a shiny embossed ice bucket for those all-essential treks to the ice machine down the hall and real drinking glasses to shatter if you feel inclined. There is also a slim shelf where packets of chocolate-coated nuts and salted crackers are lined up awaiting your spontaneous indulgence, and a big silver television mounted on the wall is ready for action, promising eight hundred plus television channels to peruse and choose. Two soft and fluffy white terry cloth robes hang in the closet when you don't want to be restricted by wearing normal clothes, and in the bathroom, a very much alive cleaning person, a twenty-something year old Hispanic woman, is busy at work, cleaning up the spoils of decadence by wiping and scrubbing the porcelain sink, anxious to remove any evidence of my tooth whitening paste, my spit and gargles. She is tidying up the cluttered bottles, too, those specially imported wrinkle-reducing face creams that don't work and the myriad of lotions and potions that have toppled over and run amok, and she is straightening up the misshapen shampoo bottles and those nasty little sachets of hair conditioner with their cheeky insistence of sticking to the shower floor tiles like rotting leaves on a patio and, I am watching her through the doorway as she sprays the his-and-her mirrors with magic glass cleaner, catching glimpses of herself, of her perfect line-free face, while she wipes the mist off in a measured way as if practicing a meditative exercise in the hotel gym. I'm guessing that she is only thinking how at a little after six o'clock, she will quickly slip out of her work shoes to don her espadrilles before she catches the six fifteen to take her along the city streets and out beyond the freeway to the mobile home where she lives with her mother. She will recount how she spent the day cleaning and wiping up after people like me, who impatiently wait, rolling their eyes, in king-size hotel rooms, waiting for her to damn well hurry up and finish before they can finally settle into the fucking king-size room, slide open the big glass doors, sit on the balcony with a view, unscrew the blue vials of vodka and toss nuts at the fat, raucous birds pecking frantically at the grass below.

Sweet Home Sweet

Dare I mention this again, but the pleasure I derived from the rooms was my only reason for carrying on. Of course I'm talking here about in the beginning when each one held a special private joy for me, and I often walked from one to the other just to check and, if necessary, rearrange, straightening a picture on the wall or reconfiguring the coffee table books and always, always taking time to perfect the best plumping methods to ensure I had the most comfortable sofa cushions and spraying the mirrors with the streak-free glass cleaner (sourced online) or to be honest simply doing nothing at all but standing in the rooms to feel them breathe as the fleeting sunlight graced the walls or the rain shattered the window panes and still, I waited, wanting to see if the rooms would either laugh or cry knowing that Miss C. and I were to be the sole observers of this private and grand showcase, staged for our eyes only.

Vapours

There were days, special days, when the rooms possessed a distinctive smell about them. This event only happened when, following a long dry spell, the clouds would finally relent and allow the rain to fall. I'm talking here about a heavy downpour, one that seemed as if it might last eternally, with the raindrops rattling away on everything and with me watching the drama from the shelter of the back porch, having stopped whatever I was doing that day. I must have been cleaning out the cupboards or ironing his shirts or weighing out bowls of golden sugar in preparation for jam making. Something to do with domesticity. The kind of necessary chores that filled my days back then. Until in the middle of that activity, I'd sense a change when a rush of cool arrogant air would pass through the open windows. It was always enough to get me to stop my task and go to stand by the back door in anticipation of what was about to occur.

The downpour fell without any pause for consideration. It showed no tenderness to the flowers in the flower beds or to the patio table and the dejected umbrella weighed down with rain that seemed to scowl at me and to say, what is your problem, do you have nothing better to do than to watch this violent inconvenience? But then, just as quickly as it had started, the rain stopped like a light switch being turned off, and in the stillness that followed, the sweet air rose from the earth in fragrant vapours mixed with hope and regret, of verbena and thyme, of sage and mint, of asters and kale and of daisies and roses and pea shoots and of children too, of children's voices singing out from the far depths of the garden beyond the fuchsia hedge. 'Mamma, Mamma,' they cried, 'the pond, the pond is full of water again.' And I would go down to where their beautiful voices hailed from to discover that, yes indeed, the pond, fully replenished, hosted a shoal of brand new smiling fish darting about in graceful, grateful circles, their silver scales glinting in the sunlight. It was at that moment, that very moment that I would look up towards the house, assured in my thinking that all the tidy rooms quietly waited for me and with said assurance in that belief, I walked across the wet silky blades of grass, like a woman who had fallen back in love with life.

Window

Today I am the high autumn tide and I just made love to the origami birds bobbing on the waves, and I am a shiny shell with tangled kelp for hair, and I am silent remembering and the remembering makes me more wistful and sorry, and I am watching a man cast his fishing rod out, I am waiting for something, I am contemplating spreading my arms out wide but I am too self-conscious, I am seeing the man with the fishing rod throw his silver catch on the shit-stained sidewalk, I am seeing death from his cruelty, I am watching life dying, I am saying to him can you not put the fish out of its misery, I am saying can you see that the fish is still alive, I am asking him not to throw the fish so carelessly onto the littered sidewalk, I am seeing him laugh at me now, I am seeing him close himself off, I am measuring up his ignorance, I am turning my collar against the chill, I am turning slightly to see a young girl standing at a window watching me watching her from across the street, the window is a window in the hostel for asylum seekers, the girl haws her breath onto the foggy glass and runs her hand around in circles to see more clearly, there is a bare light bulb like a spotlight above her head, I am seeing her turn around as if she has been called, I am imagining her crossing the room to where her mother stands, I am hoping the mother reaches out to her and picks the young girl up into her arms before she walks across to the window to close the curtains in an attempt to ward off the encroaching darkness.

Pleasure the Man

Is it really that difficult to peer through the window of one's life to watch the small home movie reel as it goes flickering and sputtering by? Is it? Tell me. Honestly what the hell does it matter if you witness your entire life on a black and white screen and you cannot, simply cannot decide to flip the switch before the ending is achieved, before the real you is revealed without much of a hullabaloo, without any heralding of when it is to be your ending? Really, look at yourself, you are just another woman with a small existence who decided to investigate what has made you this way, and therefore there is nothing exceptional about you, nothing at all, apart from the fact that you might long for a tattoo of a blue bird to adorn the diminishing branch of your arm, or that you might choose a tiny diamond to sparkle from your nose, or that you might decide to one night open up and free yourself by spreading out to caress the man beside you and to put his hardening dick in your mouth and move it around like it might even be a beautiful thing, despite it being purple and red and ugly and so out of sync with everything that you are because you are a woman, but still you allow your eyes to rest on the dick and you murmur, yes, how lovely it is. But it is not, yet still you dangle it around in your hands like a useless toy and the man swoons and responds and tries hard to resist but you have the strength to keep going, you have his dick in your hand and you play it in your hand because you are in control, moving your hand up and down and you recall the novelty of the beginning years when the dick was new and you say, sure don't you have the best dick in all of Ireland, and he, with his eyes closed, gagging and gasping with desire as you keep pulling and pushing and when he finally comes you smooth the white warm cream into your palms until it begins to get sticky and then you reach out for the paper towels to wipe it off, thinking it is just something you do, a woman does, a woman who is expected to please a man might do and afterwards when he turns away and looks at his phone and scrolls down to ESPN you might be thinking you'd both want to look at the way the sun might set or consider how the night can quickly close in but underneath that rubbish, Miss C. knew what I was really thinking. She knew that I was thinking how unfair it was that that little fuck and his hard cock came, and I did not.

Shoo, Fly, Shoo

White room, white wooden shutters, white windows and in the centre of this white room a white plinth on which to lay my white body. Bach meditates by the doorway to provide a sense of serenity. Schemes of desire briefly cross my mind, but a storm brews, too, while I wait for Master Tung to banish it. He formulates my predicaments from his neutral observation point, his sharp eyes softening briefly before resuming his calculations. Soon a long-forgotten craving presents itself: I am a young woman again with a small boy by my side, reaching for sardines on toast and ripe pears sliced into quarters. Pear juice dribbles down our chins that we never care to wipe away. And there is my mother brushing my hair in long, even strokes as I sit at her feet rubbing her legs. I, like a small obedient dog by her side, formed a circle in the comfort of slow hissing wood from the January grate and the crimson jewels of June strawberries heaped onto warm scones fresh from the oven. Oh, a welcome mishmash of memories to embrace. Surely Master Tung approves. The street manages to briefly call me back to reality, with its sing-song sounds of high-heeled clatter and slamming car doors and excited chatter from a gaggle of children passing by outside the window and then, the longed-for silence returns to all of this from my still perch in this white room where overhead a cheeky black fly plays tag with the ceiling fan. I watch and I wait.

He's a Man

On the nights when sleep eludes me I long for him to wake up so maybe we can talk things over. Talk about the way things used to be. About the times we went skinny dipping down in the valley to lie naked on the rocks to dry off. And how we would get in the car to go off anywhere whenever we felt like it, even at midnight, and drive around talking and then go home and make tea and go to bed and sleep a few hours. Does he remember any of that? He doesn't seem to. He's complicated. He's forgetful. He loses things. He's kind for the most part. He can be stubborn. He can be hateful. He is kind though. He can be terribly mean. He is a man after all. He is kind though and there are times when he can look good. But he likes to drink too much wine. He is complicated. He drives too fast. He thinks about sports and gardening. He likes chocolate. He can be mean though. He is a man. He's afraid of the washing machine. He's a man. He is kind. He can be mean. He's a man. He fixes our bed when it creaks after we make love. He is complicated. Fixing the bed is not easy. He has to take the mattress off the frame. Then he has to pull the bed away from the wall. Then he has to go downstairs and spend at least twenty minutes looking for various screwdrivers required for the procedure. He will mutter to himself doing this, opening drawers and going out to the shed and coming back in again. He is a man. He is aware of how important his job is. A bed that creaks during sex is not an ideal situation. He will go back upstairs and spend another thirty minutes unscrewing bolts and screwing them back in again. Then he'll move the bed back up against the wall and put the big mattress back on top of the frame, and then he will begin to pull and push the headboard back and forth vigorously as if he's making love to it until he's sure the creaking has stopped. He will seem pleased then for a job well done. He's kind. He can be mean though. He's a man. He is kind sometimes. I'll give him that.

Cock of the Walk

When I first came into this house all those years ago, I was eager to go from room to room, perfectly delighted with the way it presented itself to me in its virginal state and the way it practically enticed me like a new lover, excited to have all desires explored. The rooms did not know it then, but all the while I was secretly scheming over how I would change them bit by bit so that eventually, the walls and the floorboards and the ceilings and the cornices and the dark alcoves and the doorways and the windows and even the atmosphere would, over time, become what I dictated and moulded them into. And I did just that, and surprisingly the rooms consented to my wishes, happy to finally become useful and fused into a proper living entity. Because as Miss C. often suggested, rooms are malleable, for a while at least, and though this is preferable to having one's rooms cooperate like that, she was quick to remind me that there is also a chance for some scar tissue to occur, as in sometimes, the rooms can thicken and become almost impenetrable, through no fault of your own I hasten to add. This process happens in subtle ways. One day it might be how a window refuses to budge when you attempt to open it, or a lock, say with 'nary an issue' before, all of a sudden decides to stubbornly stick and is neither locked nor unlocked, or that door handle, sturdy and reliable for years, falls off in your hand and then, to make matters worse, even the plaster on the walls, seemingly starved for air, can appear to baulk at you when a mysterious and blistering mould spreads out like thick black jelly across the surface. Then that's when

the room rejects you for even thinking you might be the cock
of the walk.

A Little Bit of Whimsy

How bright and airy those rooms appeared to me in the seemingly unending days of summer. Oh yes, they were, and cosy and curtained in the dark, eternal months of winter. But once spring came I would open all the windows to air out the rooms and allow the birdsong in. When autumn came along, well, it was all about orange and golden curlicues and nutty browns in wicker baskets, and I'd gather them up into bundles of crunchy fallen leaves to strew about so that I could walk through them, kicking the colours to scatter like new decorations landing at will on the sofa and the tables and mantelpiece and the photographs of the way we used to be. It was so simple yet so effective. That's what he used to say when he saw me doing that. Then he'd amble away from me, shaking his head and tut-tutting his mildly amused disapproval as he measured out extended and convoluted theories on this and that, disappearing into the bowels of our house, mumbling something to himself, always mumbling away to himself.

Lava

I never understood where the anger came from. But one day when I woke up it was there, bubbling beneath the surface like lava preparing for an eruption. Anger throws you off balance. You feel like a ship that hasn't been properly loaded with its cargo, and so everything is a little lopsided. Equilibrium becomes a thing of the past. Miss C. knew only too well that I was never like that before. Long ago in all those rooms, anger was an alien emotion that stayed way out beyond the walls. In those days it was something that belonged to other people. But wait. Maybe anger was there all that time, skulking around in the shadows, ready to pounce when the right opportunity came along when I least expected it to surface. Yes, it must have been there alright, holding its breath.

Imagine if you thought you could lock a bold child into a pitch-dark room to teach him a lesson. You know how it goes. The luring him in with the promise of milk and cookies, but once you get him inside, you leave quickly, shut the door behind you and turn the key. But guess what? When you think he's learned his lesson and the kid is eventually allowed to go free, you see that the kid is bolder than ever, and maybe he might even just try to kill you because when he was in the dark room, he grew angry and resentful while he heard you outside whistling a lovely little tune and going about your business as if all was well with the world, as you open the windows to allow the fresh, clean air to engulf the room. All the while little Johnny continues to fume in his temporary prison, all the while planning how he will unleash his new anger when he gets out, and you're still stupidly thinking I'm doing little Johnny a favour. He will learn from this. A locked room is the beginning for little Johnny, and when he comes out he will be a new person. I am sure I must have been that little Johnny who was waiting for someone to turn the key and open the door to let me out. I was coy at first, anxious to appear as my normal self, but beware, once the lid is lifted, lava moves fast, like the blink of an eye.

A Game of Footsie

Carry on now. There are bound to have been moments when you wonder how it all began. When those unexpected occurrences sidle up like venomous snakes ready to bite you in the neck or hover outside the window in the darkness planning how they might eventually get at you, observing you in the seconds and minutes as you go about the evening, gauging how long it will take for you to fall, anxiously fidgeting from foot to foot in the darkness, anticipating that perfect opportunity to nail you once and for all. But now that I have presented this predicament, I see that it could have been on one of those nights when Dr. J. and his glorious wife, M., came over for dinner. Dr. J. a renowned psychiatrist and a newly recruited member of faculty who enjoyed his wine, while M., his wife, a life coach, ran a thriving practice and wore far too many glittering pieces of jewellery, naturally bestowed upon her by aforementioned spouse.

It was fun to entertain, to have my mind consumed with the planning of the menu, and the various lists I made up to remind me to chill the wine, and to make sure the candles were lit, and to perfect the salad dressing, and to only choose duck breasts that were extra plump, and to be sure to make a black cherry sauce well in advance so as to compliment the duck, and to prepare my famous Potatoes Dauphinoise, easy on the garlic now, and not to forget to defrost the hors d'oeuvres, and to fill the little glass bowls with salted nuts, and to make the perfect cheesecake with a glazed fruit topping, and to have plenty of chilled sparkling water to hand, and to use the best linen and the crystal glasses, and the this and the that, so when the ding dong of the doorbell goes, I'm still in a fluster but a good fluster, and the guests coming in with a great gusto about them, and I smelling the fresh evening air on them, and they are looking festive and expectant and eager to have a social gathering, and I giving both of them a little peck on each cheek the way you are supposed to do, and I tell them that they are so welcome and they settle in easily, you could say fluidly like fish in a stream, and they say everything looks wonderful, and look at your room, and its wonderful too, and did you get the place recently decorated, and they ask what colour is that on the wall and I say it is Connecticut Blue, and they ooh and ahh above the click and clack of the wine glasses, and the toasts that go back and forth in cheers with dinner flowing seamlessly on, and I draw the curtains and the room gets smaller and more intimate and I feel so relaxed now, and all the doors are open in my mind and the wine keeps coming, and I am sitting beside Dr. J. and I am dying to ask him if he has ever met anyone who thinks about rooms like I do, but I don't. Instead I slice up the New York cheesecake that I made the day before, and he says, this is wonderful and did you make it from scratch, and I am sitting right beside him, and he is studying me, and I pretend I do not notice nor care and the candles are so soft, and the music is moody, something jazzy, and then I feel his foot moving slowly back and forth over mine beneath the dishevelled table and the embroidered white linen table cloth that my mother left me as an heirloom, and I begin to realise that all along he, Dr. J., was strategically easing his feet free from his sensible black shoes to allow them to play a slow, teasing, methodical game of footsie with me and it feels like the most natural thing in the world, and all the while the other two are talking about an art exhibition they have both seen. And I don't know why I allowed Dr. J. to continue to run his tartan cashmere-clad foot over mine as he licked his lips and most sincerely pleaded for another slice of cake. I honestly don't. Neither did Miss C.

Midnight

I feel compelled at this point to reveal that there were many days when I allowed myself to forget about anything to do with the matters that normally consumed me, and so to empty out my thoughts, I'd turn the lights off on them and close the doors so that they sat unused, devoid of attention. Then he and I were free to dance so effortlessly into the proper rooms waiting on the outside, where life shone. And there was that special way he could look at me and lock my gaze with his grey, green eyes that dared me to take my clothes off and go lie down alongside him on the cool grass in the back garden late at night beneath a new moon. Yes. It happened. When the rooms had no boundaries, and the sky fell down on top of us and ceilinged us with its midnight blue curtain and we fucked and laughed and fucked again. And when the nights came in with the curtains drawn and the fire lit and the children tucked safely into their beds, the light throwing shadows on the walls had us reminisce about the early days and the way we lay sprawled on the rocks by the creek, two long-legged spiders soaking up the sun. We were selfish. We were happy. We only saw each moment. We wanted nothing more than each other.

Glass

I finally got around to clearing up the glass. Although one has to be careful. Vigilance with broken glass is an absolute necessity. Did you know that glass happens to be one of the few things in life that is more lethal when it breaks into small fragments than when it breaks into bigger ones? Take that day when I broke a drinking glass that sat innocently on the draining board minding its own business, smugly drying itself in the afternoon sunlight. Just as I picked it up, Miss C., in a typical bout of making trouble, decided to poke me in the back to cause the glass to slide like a restless toddler out of my arms. The glass fell onto the tiled kitchen floor, where it shattered into a thousand pieces. There were big, bold shards and invisible, miniscule shards all over the tea towel and the windowsill and the floor, the sink, the spice rack, the plants, beneath the presses, in the corners, everywhere it could possibly find a place to settle. I spent ages picking it up. I even got out the Hoover to vacuum up any sneaky stray bits of glass, but if anything, the pieces seemed to multiply. What's worse, one piece of glass stuck in my thumb, and I dug and picked at it until a sore developed, and then the sore turned into an angry gaping hole, and I still couldn't find the piece even though I knew it was there because the glass told me it was there by causing a little pricking sensation every now and then just as a tease, as if to say, 'now don't you relax, I'm still here'. I was aware, and it is a well-known fact, that if you don't get a piece of glass out, it will poison your system. It will plan its course for a short period before it begins a slow trawl up into the canals of your veins to finally clog the very last breath in your being. But I am not writing this down because of the shard in my thumb. No, I am not, and besides, I can't delve into something as important as this straight away. Experience tells me that you have to weigh it all out. You could say it is akin to the preparation required for the baking of a cake. Only a fool doesn't take time to read the entire recipe first and then take the time to measure out all of the ingredients before she begins to make the cake. And only the wisest of mammas know that you never tell a man anything important until after he's been fed. They are right about that. But that's beside the point. So let's see, where was I? Oh yes, now, if I told you what happened from the end to the beginning it might all become clear. That is to me, at least. If I replayed the glass shards falling to the floor, then breaking on the side of the draining board, then dropping out of my hand to when it first sat innocently and serenely on the draining board in the warmth of the afternoon sunlight when I put it there to dry in the first place, I would have seen that the still wet drinking glass had, (after I was so rudely prodded by Miss C.), a fair chance of falling out of my hands when I picked it up and that it had, at the very least, an eighty per cent chance of breaking. But it doesn't work like that, does it? We never see the endings first, do we? Yes. We are always much more obsessed with the beginnings. Forever ensuring everything is in proper order, we never even consider the consequences say, of going from room to room and opening and closing the doors again once we look inside to check all is in order. But that very second after you check and close the door to walk away is the moment something in that room dislodges. Then the something that is the unstoppable begins. Subtle at first but ultimately one that builds up over time, to gain momentum, as the fragments and disarrays and loose ends gather until they eventually become something of significance. That is when you stop and notice the end result. But by then it is usually too late.

The Atmosphere

They threatened to topple down on me. Of course I'm referring to walls, glass, wood and furniture. Those bloody mate-
rials guilty of making up the weight of the atmosphere. Then
take into account the colour and mood and memories that
are absolutely bound, without even realising it, to weigh you
down too. Thankfully though, many rooms are strong: like
the hands of a woman or that brave face we put on ourselves
even though inside we secretly carry the worries and unspo-
ken words we cannot, will not, ever express. And what about
all the stuff that lodges in corners and underneath stones and
in between the bricks and mortar that will never ever have
a chance of being revealed again? Therefore, with all of the
above in mind, I knew more than anyone that I needed to
tread carefully because the rooms might, if I was not careful,
come at me all at once. To reiterate, rooms can fall on you like
heavy rocks and crush you back down. And with this grand
groundbreaking revelation duly noted, I resolved to allow the
rooms to gradually appear like random gifts of a sort. As if to
say remember me? Do you recall that time in that room and
that time and that time and that time? And remember that
time when you...? And throughout this period I urged Miss C.
to remain alert and aware of how the rooms required so much
of our undivided attention.

Look at Yourself

You can learn so much about yourself if you are brave enough to look in the mirror for a longish time. Let me be clear; I'm not talking about a glance you might make when you're smoothing out your eyebrows, adding a little lipstick, or dab dabbing at something like a stain or a bit of fluff sticking to your collar. To really look at yourself in the mirror you must first remove any distractions like makeup and clothing. Then, once naked, permit your eyes to first quickly scan your body before you properly begin. Good. Then the first move is to wiggle your toes while taking note of how the arches of your feet are, well, a glorious feat (forgive the pun) of architectural design and that the smooth skin and veined lattice beneath remind you of delicate butterfly wings. Then slowly working your way up, travel across the tiny mounds of ankle to the shins, then the knees , the thighs and of course lingering on that special place between, where you momentarily ponder on what is so special about it, why it is so desired and what it has produced in its magnificent resilience, but caution, don't linger for too long, no keep going, travelling onward to your belly button, pausing before considering the soft curve of your hips and waistline, stoic in its presentation, leading you higher, past the ribs where you allow your eyes to rest on the breasts and to look at them, to really look at them and touch them too by running your hands around their lovely soft silkiness, because they are just magnificent to hold, to feel their powerful heave in your hands, to measure the weight and the sag of time, to tease the nipples briefly before spreading each arm out wide to see how long and graceful they appear, as if ready for flight, so capable to carry you forward, and moving on, you explore your neck, and gently smooth its elegance upward to your chin, out to your lobes, soft and warm like kittens ears, and then you feel the sinews in your ears too and think how amazing they are, fine yet strong, until finally running your fingers along your lips and up to your nose, the nostrils breathing warm air on your fingertips, you look directly into your eyes and see how blue and wide open they are, full of impressions and memories so vivid that you cannot believe they are real anymore, but you keep on looking until the glass slowly opens up to beckon you in, leaving behind tangled shadows dancing wildly on the walls.

Emptiness

I'm writing all of this down in the room where the children slept. There were two small beds separated by a table, and there was me, the mother hen, cluck-clucking and constantly fussing and checking on them when the sickness days came. Up and down the stairs I went to measure the dips and soars of temperatures. Clever me to think of putting my lips to burning foreheads and to run them back and forth in a gauge to discern discomfort. And those make-believe stories I told aloud for their ears only. And then the learning-to-read time came along. It came so fast. Slap in the face, that was. No more need for Momma to read. Then learning to drive came along, and girlfriend and no more need for Momma to cry to. Then half-packed suitcases and travel far and wide, and no more need for Momma, period. These memories hang in the air in this room. Let them dangle like deflated balloons. It is not far away enough. Yes. It's still the early days to the beginning of the ending.

Room.Rum.Ruim. Raum.

Definition:

a space that can be occupied or where something can be done. Synonyms: space, free space, headroom, legroom, area, territory, expanse, extent, volume, scope, capacity, margin, leeway, latitude, freedom.

&

NOTES TO SELF:

COPIED FROM

'HOW TO MAKE THE MOST OF ROOMS'

(A GIFT FROM MOTHER–IN-LAW)

Colour. Dark colours create a sense of intimacy appropriate to small spaces; lighter colours provide the ease and openness that large rooms require.

~~~Blue is a sedative said to calm anxiety.~~~

(Latter highlighted in a bright orange marker)

Red makes time move more slowly.

Yellow improves students' grades.

Note: your colour choices are probably limited by upholstery, carpets, artwork. Use these as inspiration.

NB: White is seldom the most satisfying solution.

Do you want a soft room or a cosy room?

Will you be thinking and working in it or sleeping in it?

What kind of lighting do you want? Ambient? Task? Or decorative?

The play of light and shadow over their surfaces gives nuance to the colour.

Movement from room to room should be a fluid experience filled with subtle experiences and no jarring surprises.

(Latter queried by several question marks).

When the world outside feels too harsh, take refuge in a soothing bath or a plump soft bed.

(Latter underlined with conviction).

Homemaker

Sorry to say, but there are days when I am unable to proceed. It's as if none of this existed, and what I have written and attempt to write further might just merely be but a figment of my imagination. It is as if what I attempt to recall is something only conjured up by some form of quiet desperation. During this time I imagine a room with nothing in it. It is a pure white floating room with me in the middle, breathing slowly and deeply in and out until I close my eyes and relax. Then it comes. A room. Dark this time. Night. Safe. I am in a distant city preparing to go out. I wear a long silk dress that reaches almost down to my ankles, and long green earrings sparkle from my earlobes. I apply oil of bergamot to my pulse spots and at the base of my spine. I am sensual, so womanly. And then it stops. Nothing. Only this room, the one I write from. This will be a memory someday, too, where I'm stuck between the concrete blocks trying to find the window. The children gone, and what is left? What do you do, they asked, what about your career? Miss C. always sniggered when that particular question was posed. And I replied confidently, mother, I'm a mother. That's it, ha, ha, they laughing amongst themselves during their regular coffee morning meetings. Is that all she ever did with her life? Yes, me. The one and only purveyor of rooms supreme? The chief bottle-washer extraordinaire? Sir, ahem, just a moment now, let me tell you. Yes, I was all of that and the cleaner-upper of vomit, and reliable provider of cough medicines come midwinter, buyer of sandals and shorts, and experienced tour operator to beach for necessary activities in summer, wiper-down of bottoms and snot and table tops, and pending patent of top scouring techniques of all sinks, although I did tend to specialise in ceramics, undisputed vacuuming expert, window cleaner supreme, and problem solver of impossible to remove toilet bowl stains, taxi driver, interior designer and accomplished cook who could turn a can of beans into a gourmet dish in five minutes, second to none laundry operator, best shoulder to cry on for miles around, and so overall a domestic goddess without any doubt. Yes. That was me with rooms to prove it.

Impressive record to be sure. Yes, sir. Then what? All that and for nothing, it seems. And where is my certificate? My honours degree for all that devotion to going in and around and down and out and up and over and back around again and again before tumbling down a hillside of yellow daisies until the sky and the house full of rooms and the kids and the man are mixed inside to become a magical kaleidoscope spinning with hope into some kind of eternal nothingness.

Dog Days

Do you know how when the dog jumps up onto the bed to lie down beside you, and you start to pet her all along her small body, stopping briefly to tickle her under her chin and then running your fingers lightly along her tiny little back you start talking softly to her, but after a while, well what does she do, but stand up and move away from you to settle herself at the other end of the bed, as if you never existed? Well, I wish I could do that. Move away from the pawing. Spread myself out and prohibit all trespassers. Yes, to be left alone, to sigh peacefully, to stretch out my bones, glad for once that I can close my eyes and expect nothing.

Woman at Sink

I will, for now if you please, remain in the good-memory rooms where I can comfortably recall watching him over the four seasons of this lifetime, from this window, in this room, this kitchen, in this house. That window was once like a television screen that held a permanent picture of him so that it might as well have been a constant rolling documentary of his life. Sometimes the pictures were delivered clearly with enviable definition, while other times, the pictures blurred, became static and seemed to struggle to proceed. Nonetheless, I loved standing at that window, watching him as he went through the motions of his existence. A little-known fact here, but did you know that every woman should insist on having her kitchen sink placed beneath a window? It is truly a recommendation worth noting as it becomes an essential addition. The viewing becomes practically therapeutic if you really want to know. Even Miss C. agreed with that philosophy. And besides, the window relieved so much for me, alienated the trouble brewing beneath it, if one had the foresight, the capacity to see into the future. Some don't want to see or have that capacity to see at the time.

I met a woman once, and she told me that she felt sure there was an invisible chain that bound her between her kitchen sink and the kitchen counter. Everyday she'd drag that chain back across the small floor space, toiling the hours away, resentful of the chain and all that it represented to her. I wanted to ask her if she could have looked out the window, but then

I realised there wasn't a window above her sink. Maybe she could have found a key or some other way to untie the chain. During the latter days of our separate journey, I saw her occasionally walking about in the city, all along the disjointed cobbled streets. Once I encountered her face to face, and I smiled at her, but she walked by as if she hadn't recognised me. I turned to follow her and noticed how she did not stall or hesitate, and I admit she did appear to walk with a new purpose. Perhaps she had severed her own chain after all.

I know though that the window above my kitchen sink never let me down. There was so much to look out at, and as I've already revealed, I loved to watch him each season coming and going like it was an all-important part of the plan. Whenever an opportunity arose, especially in spring, he would practically change career overnight to become a wheelbarrow operator set to heaving bags of soil and compost across the lawn and down past the silvery willows. I'm sure his head was close to bursting with it being so full of garden plans and activities needing to be done as he dug and tossed spades of soil and stood back and put his hands on his hips to look around him, and up at the sky, and towards the old dried up lake at the back of the field. I admit that I'd want him then, dirt and all. I'd want him to come up to me and push open the back door and walk over to the sink where I stood looking out, hoping to find something, and he would grab me to him from behind as if I was someone he had to hold onto like a drowning man, and then he'd push up my skirt and enter me and quickly come. He never lingered but simply pulled his trousers back up and returned to his composting and the soil as if it was all a part of the way it was supposed to be. Yes, I can still picture how he'd put his hands rough and still warm with new soil back into his pockets while his grey–green eyes kept a constant watch on the scheming black clouds far away on the western horizon. And all the time he whistled some odd little ditty, 'if I should see you on the street sometime...', and it was then I wished the seasons would come into the room, slowly seep underneath the gap in the door, to eventually swirl up in front of me like a great big cauldron of thoughts and goings on and memories and more thoughts that I could carry with me during the seconds and the minutes and the hours and the mornings and the afternoons and the nights and the weeks and the months and the seasons and the years and the birthdays and the funerals and the joy and the sadness and the wanting and the needing and the screaming and the laughing and, and, and I'd be swept into the frenzy of those times with him, and we'd be dancing around in brilliant colours, flowing about the kitchen and down the hall and into the rooms. And then before anything else could happen, it all went swoosh when he came back into the house, and everything turned black and white again with shades of grey. I often watched him cross the kitchen floor as if in slow motion, switching on the radio to listen to the news, washing his hands and looking out the window while a voice in the background would announce how twenty people were killed in a terror attack on a busy street, just then, that very second in a faraway city. Everything resumed itself back to normal then. I behaved again. The rooms behaved again too. The rooms and I were a bunch of unruly students hushing themselves, hurrying back to our desks because the Master was about to hurl himself back into the classroom after running out for a second. Yes, that is what it was like. Not often but now and then, that's for sure.

I Wish

Do you ever wish you could go back? Begin all over again, wake up in the morning a brand new woman and sit up, stretch your arms out wide and over your head and yawn, a big wide stupid silly kind of a yawn and then shut your eyes, open your eyes and still feel the same as you did before you shut them, before you put your feet on the floor, spread out your toes, stand, breathe and allow half a smile before you make your way down the stairs to glide across the linoleum floor, put the kettle on and watch the steam rise while you wipe away the condensation on the glass?

I do.

Blue and Green Sea Glass

With regard to the matters of interior design, I turned to Miss
C. and said, look here, you can help me as I take this child's
drawing, this simple crayon drawing of a house with squares
for windows and an impossibly tall red door. See the chimney
pot with black smoke coming out and the crooked tree on a
patch of brown grass. Now, can you see a woman's face at one
of the windows? Well, so you must understand why I want to
put that drawing on the uppermost part of the wall facing the
fireplace. It only seems fitting that I will add a photograph of
a loyal and companionable dog. Note how it induces a sense
of intense pleasure when she rests her tiny head on your lap
to listen intently as you read aloud from a book of poems. I
think I will put that right beside the child's drawing of the
house. Now, place that voice, yes that voice, the one calling
out your name from an ornate alcove, in the far bottom left-
hand corner. Attach the smell of garlic and butter rising from
a pan close by. That picture he took of me looking calm as I
leaned gracefully on a balcony facing the sea before I turned
around smiling to embrace him should be placed high up in
the north-end corner. And Miss C., do please try, without delay, to hang the clang of church bells, heralding evening
prayers, beneath the devoted dog dreaming on my lap. Most
importantly of all we must take extreme care to manoeuvre
the various pieces of blue and green glass, gathered over time
from shores, close by and distant, and employ them to form a
zigzag of no importance, but just do it, simply for the pleasure of doing it. Then place it in the centre of the wall, inter-

spersed with intricate pearly shells of pink and white. Finally, make a space for many mirrors so that the reflections will remind us how all rooms eventually lead to other rooms, but obviously only if you really want them to.

The View

These days we never consider the view. But we did once after we came here from the distant desert landscape. Back then the view was something to boast about. 'Look, come on upstairs,' we'd urge our house guests, 'you have to see our stunning view.' And when they did, they were amazed to see the low mountains to the south and the sea gleaming in the foreground and how everything changed colour, with different shades of grey one minute, then suddenly switching into a rainbow of blues and varying greens, the next. One look and the sky would be bright and splendid, and the next sullen and moody, spattered with drizzles of snow in winter and blushes of purple come summertime.

The view. My god, what a view to devour. Easy to dally by the window and look out. Rest those weary elbows on the sill and imbibe the pure pleasure instilled within. Call out his name to come see the view. Insist he do so right that minute so that you can both agree on your mutual good fortune. Everyone craves a room with a view. We have one now, we'd say delightedly, like two self-satisfied schemers. Then what would he do? Well, he'd hold me to him with his arm around my waist and continue to look out at our view. And then, discovering to his delight that I was not wearing a bra, he'd run his hand beneath my blouse to fondle my breasts, so intensely that he might as well have been gently probing an avocado at the store, lost in thought while my nipples surged with longing. It was easy to come then. All I had to contend with was in that room with

the view and his hand caressing my breast and the evening
June sky slowly unfolding itself into an array of pink and timid
orange peel clouds. And all the time as he kept looking out at
the view, I shut my eyes. I shut them tight.

Don't Call Me Dear

The checkout person at the store called me Dear again. I was there to buy gorgonzola cheese and white wine and great black and green grapes and hummus. I also bought a small bunch of sweet Williams, and I felt temporarily happy because I was free to go into a store and buy whatever I wanted to buy and bring it home to the rooms where I could eat them undisturbed. While I was standing in the checkout queue, I observed the people in the queue, and not one of them looked like a Dear to me. I was also taking note of the checkout woman bagging the goodies for people and taking their money, and she didn't look like a Dear either. I also noted that not once did she call any of the customers Dear. Then my turn came, and after I had paid for the groceries and she was handing me my change, she said, thank you, my Dear. I was furious. I wanted to hit her so badly, but I didn't, of course. Instead I said, don't call me that, and she said, what, and I said, Dear, don't call me Dear, you called me Dear, and I really hate being called Dear, you will not dare to put me into the Dear room now or ever, and so she said, my apologies, Miss, before she turned away like she'd already forgotten me and started dealing with the next person. I left practically blinded by rage. You see, I have my reasons not wanting to be called Dear. Who wants to be called Dear? Jesus Christ. Another beginning.

A Hotel Overlooking the River

After that initial evening of entertaining Dr. J. and his glorious wife, and following the subsequent clandestine game of delicious footsie, I received, in the course of a couple of weeks, several intimate messages from him. And following those somewhat naughty admissions, a most furtive phone call ensued where he suggested we meet up in a hotel room in another town. He suggested this by speaking to me in a very low and, now that I come to think of it, a strangely disappointing matter-of-fact voice. He instructed me to avail of the express train to this town where nobody knew him and henceforth to proceed to a hotel by the river that was quite impersonal. He said he was able to make a reservation without any human contact whatsoever, and he figured that was a plus in his plans. It wasn't hard for me to agree with his proposal, and I assured him I would take the express train to the town where nobody knew him, and then take a cab to the hotel by the river that was quite impersonal. Yes, I said, I will wear something that doesn't stand out. I will take it down a peg or two. Yes, I said, I absolutely have something dull and boring to wear that will not draw attention. Yes, we were speaking in very matter-of-fact voices. Yes, I concurred that I would take the glass elevator in the hotel overlooking the river that was quite impersonal to the third floor. Yes, I agreed with him when he warned me about the horrible carpets. Floral carpets are invariably gauche. Yes, I will keep to the left and count ten doors down until I arrive at room three-four-three and knock three times in swift succession, and I will wait until I hear him ask is that you? And yes, I will respond, yes, Dr. J. It is I. Good, well that's that, he said and hung up. Blank.

Rotten Apples

Have you ever gone to the store to buy a bag of cooking apples where your goal is to naturally choose the biggest, greenest, most blemish-free tart apples you can find? You carefully pick each one and easily fill a paper bag with them. When you get home you place them ever so lovingly into a well-chosen earthenware bowl. You place the bowl in the centre of the kitchen table. Listen, you know this to be true. Even though you haven't baked anything for quite some time, you have great plans for the apples; trying to decide if you will make apple crumble, apple fool, apple fritters or maybe attempt some apple and olive oil muffins or how about a good old fashioned apple pie or, a to die for apple cobbler or maybe, yes, that's it, done deal, a sticky toffee apple pudding.

Each day as you pass by the bowl, you're thinking I must make that pudding soon. But you don't. You get distracted. Then a week passes, and before you know it, three weeks have passed since you first put the apples in the bowl, smack dab in the centre of the table. Now though you begin to notice how small brown blemishes are starting to appear on the surface of the apples. You pick one up to examine it and remark to yourself, yes, I must use them soon before it's too late. At the very least I can make apple sauce with them. But it doesn't happen because you get distracted until the very next day when a strong smell of rotting apples fills the room. You pick up one of the apples and find if you poke a finger through the pulpy flesh, it comes out on the other side with hardly any effort whatsoever. It disgusts you. And the smell in the room is so putrid that you have to open the window and throw the rotten apples in the bin.

Note: fruit takes a while to decay. So much time passes by without you ever noticing it. Decay is renowned for being quiet and stealthy, and after that? Well, it really is only a matter of time.

Waiting for Monday

It's hard to believe that at one time I proclaimed this house to be way too small for a growing family. How little foresight I had back then to think how I went on and on about it when nowadays it is like living in a big empty church haunted by voices echoing feeble prayers and pious hymns, robotically sung by obedient women with dents in their knees, no doubt the result of time spent kneeling on hard pine protesting their guilt. There are days, especially Sundays, when I admit that I want to find the tiniest and most remote corner of this house where I would if I could, high above the rafters, find a place and crawl in the way spiders do, curl myself up into a ball and settle into a silent web so that I don't fall down.

I never liked Sundays when the children moved away to carry on with their own lives. That meant the end of Sunday spins out to the steely grey mountains and the anticipated stops at remote country pubs to order tall glasses of red lemonade with stripy bubble-making straws. Once the children moved on, there were no more sizzles of juicy Sunday roasts or battles for the funnies section that came tumbling out of the newspaper in front of the Sunday fires, the tussles on the rug, the inevitable tears and the drama of making up. Sure, they visit occasionally when time allows, but they never stay long. Always busy with wives and kids and plans and vacations and dreams and their own rooms, I suppose. All the things we had. The things I thought we had.

I wish someone had whispered it in my ear to warn me that all the fuss of life is only a long storm, and when you look back, to finally have space to consider, you find that you are secretly wondering what it was all about rushing through those incessant school runs and birthday parties and dinner parties and barbecues and sickness and teenage tantrums and cluttered rooms and weddings and funerals and grief and sex and longing and wishing and planting and mulching and loving and money issues and holidays and emergency rooms and hand holding and pushing and tugging and promises and regrets, that eventually it ends up like this Sunday in this Sunday room waiting for Monday.

Why Did She Not Warn Me?

It is time to admit how I was often disappointed in Miss C. Writing this down now, trying to figure it all out, I wonder, as my best friend, my sole confidante, why she never once warned me of the impending drama. Surely she could have simply tapped me on the shoulder and said, stop, the game is over, enough. Every opportunity was available for her to pull me aside into a dark lonely corner in some neglected room, or a cold, abandoned attic room, somewhere with a small iron bed in the corner, or a luxurious room with a blazing fire in the hearth, or a herb-scented bathroom, or a kitchen bathed in aromas of exotic spices, anywhere, anywhere, where she could have taken me aside and insisted that I avoid the path I seemed bent on following. She knew all about that uneven, hazardous path cleverly luring me past doors permanently shut against the light to the eventual knocker, that persistent knocker rapping ever so cunningly and assuredly in the fast and strengthening gales of my mind.

Dream

Reminder: on 'room-free days' my life presented itself as perfectly doable. I was contented and prepared to be what I was expected to be. On the perfectly doable days, I allowed everything room related to lie unprovoked within me, so to speak. I wanted it all to be right. By it, I mean our life together, albeit with Miss C., stubbornly ever-present behind my back.

Whenever he touched me on those doable days, I allowed his hand to rest until it felt like a candle had been lit just before darkness releasing me from all imposed restrictions, with the rooms retreating into the background where they remained dormant, deep in my psyche, leaving only a sense of peace and rest behind and a confidence in knowing the rooms would only resume significance when I called upon them to do so. All I can say is that on those days, I chose to imagine the walls liquefying into cool, fresh ocean water pulsing with a new energy that entered me and urged me to stretch out my arms, tilt back my head and float without any surfaces to hem me in. This was a joyful place without ceilings that revealed a vista of endless cloud-free skies permitting me to relish a little reprieve to find:

I floated

I breathed freely

I trusted

I was free

I was clearly buoyant

I became translucent

I was mother of pearl

I was a silver-scaled fish

I was a young woman once again

I was making a sandwich

I was laughing uncontrollably

I was running upstairs

I was sliding down a banister

I was holding my mother's hand

I was sitting on a window seat basking in sunlight

I was picking daisies to make a daisy chain

I was calling out to a dog across a field

I was humming a tune

I was counting the days

I was watching a grey and white seagull swoop

I was thinking about Rothko then

I was buying a new dress

I was making ratatouille

I was in a city that never slept

I was giving birth

I was turning to see

I was picking up a pen to write

I was outside looking in

I was breastfeeding

I was carefully laying bits of driftwood and shells on a window sill

I was choosing a bottle of wine

I was turning to the next page

I was dabbing perfume on my wrists

I was inhaling the scent

I was planning to buy gifts

I was holding a child's hand

I was falling in love

I was touching him

I was touching myself

I was blowing candles out on a pink cake

I was saying look, two rainbows all at once

I was arranging tulips in a vase

I was saying I love you

I was alive

I was

I was

and

then

I

WOKE

UP.

Verbal Copulation

In total I met Dr. J. on two occasions. It was a lot easier than I'd imagined it to be. I suppose it helped matters that the express train left on an hourly basis for the town where nobody knew him. And not for a minute did I second guess what I was about to do. At home Husband rarely enquired what my plans entailed for the day, and so I proceeded like an innocent participant in an interactive game might do, believing that nobody would really be too upset. After all I was only play-acting for a little distraction to pass the time.

Anyhow on that appointed day, when I got to room three-four-three, I knocked three times (as instructed) on the door of the room of the hotel by the river that was quite impersonal. It crossed my mind that he wasn't there and somebody was playing a bad joke on me, but then I heard a male voice ask, is that you? I replied yes, Dr. J., it is I. I remember winking at Miss C. who, for once, looked uncharacteristically unsure of herself. When Dr. J. opened the door I was shocked to see how much older and serious he appeared to be in the rawness of daylight. He was wearing a black turtle neck sweater, and okay, black turtle neck sweaters do tend to make men seem more serious than they actually are. I should know. Anyway, he ushered me in without any greeting and then he sat on the only armchair by the window with its dirty, clouded windowpane overlooking the river. I stood by the door, not really knowing what to do. My tote bag by my feet, I might as well have been on a station platform waiting for the next train. I said, it's a nice day, isn't it, Dr. J., trying to sound carefree, but my voice came out like a robot. I asked him if he could open the window. He tried, but it refused to budge. I sat on the bed to take off my shoes. I could feel his eyes on me without me looking straight back at him. Eventually he spoke but in a voice that I could not recall from the evening of the dinner party. No, this time he distinctly spoke in a practitioner's voice, removed and clinical as he had on the phone and said, I want you to please relax. I am going to ask you something, slight cough here from him, ahem, as he attempted to clear his throat before proceeding. I want you to answer me honestly. Have you ever heard of verbal copulation? No, I said, I have no idea what that is. I grew tense as he spoke to me like a professor who had sheets of lecture notes in his hands, with me, the student, listening carefully because I didn't want to miss something important. Verbal copulation, stressing the words, is an interest of mine, he said, though not much is known about it, and therefore my new, updated research paper will focus solely on the recruited candidates, and lowering his voice, he added, with you of high interest of course. Their reaction to the stimuli provided will be invaluable. There will be no need to fully undress during these sessions. No need at all. We will begin shortly, but first I want you to try to clear your head of all that has gone before this room, and we will both sit here for five minutes before we commence.

I lay down on the bed and looked straight up at the ceiling. I tried to think of nothing. I tried desperately to rid my mind of all the clutter and the rooms and the memories that kept bombarding it, but it was impossible. I imagined it could have been possible, in the intimacy of his arms, to have asked him about the rooms and what they meant and why I constantly thought about them. But then I began to remember the night he came to dinner with his wife, M., the life coach in the tight skirt and how thrilling it was to feel his foot rubbing against mine and how he had desired me beneath the table and the table cloth and how here we were in room three-four-three in a hotel by a river that was quite impersonal in a town where nobody knew him and that alone was so exciting and beyond belief. The minutes dragged before he stood up and approached the bed, pacing in a priestly way while speaking in that low, neutral, emotionless voice;

He said, I must say you're looking very attractive today.

I said, thank you, Dr.J., so do you.

I wanted you from the first time I saw you, he said.

I wanted you too, I said.

Why did you, he asked as he scratched his chin.

I said, I don't know why, I just did, maybe because you were interested in me, you spoke to me. Not many people do.

I wanted you that night, he said.

I wanted you the first time I saw you when I walked into your home and into that room that suited you so well.

I wanted to put my hand under your dress and run it up to your panties that night when we were sitting together at the dinner table. Do you remember?

Yes, I remember; I wanted you too, I said.

Then Dr. J. suggested we should meditate on our little chat, our little 'tété a tété', walked over to the window to touch the window pane tenderly in what looked like a feeble attempt to erase the tainted glass with his hands and enable him to peer down at the slow flowing nameless river below.

How are you feeling now? Hmm? Relaxed? Turned on?

Pretty good, I said. My mind was only thinking about what he'd said. That I was picturing him running his hand up along my leg and right up into my panties and I was wet and I hadn't been in quite a while.

I was also imagining him smiling across the table at his wife, M. the life coach, and her not knowing that his hands were in my panties.

Good, he said, very good and rubbed his busy paws together as if something special had been achieved. That will be it for today. This was stage one of our meeting. We will continue in two weeks' time. Try not to be late. I only have the room for a limited amount of time, and with that he opened the door to let me out. Miss C. looked at me and shrugged before making one of her funny faces. She stuck two fingers up at him just as he was turning around while he frantically adjusted the collar of his turtle neck to ensure the crease was 'just so'.

All Aboard

So what is to become of the future rooms? Dare I try to envision that and journey down the remaining length of corridor to discover how some doors, still ajar, might be anxiously attempting to lure me in? Do I stand outside these doors questioning whether I might enter, or am I so fearful that I remain motionless in the darkened space, without ever discovering what lies beyond those unexplored doors? But what if I accept the temptation to look inside as a quick inspection of sorts? A scenario of one foot in and one foot out, so to speak? Because is it not the case that we have little or no say in our destiny? Is it, to be precise, a case that once the train has left the station, and you are safely ensconced in your window seat, it quickly dawns on you that you've forgotten why and where you are going, and when you call the train conductor over to clarify matters, she only reveals, after the final whistle has blown and the train in motion, that you have boarded a bullet train? Realising it doesn't stop until you get to the destination, you reluctantly sit back down and try to figure out where you are going by looking out the window, but the train is travelling at such a speed that you cannot learn anything from the countryside as it becomes blurred like a watercolour painting, and so you look straight ahead and stay that way until you arrive at the station. Noticing, as you disembark, how everyone appears to be walking in one direction (as if aware they have no choice in the matter), you walk alongside them, accepting that if you tried to go in the opposite direction, it would be an impossibility with the force from the masses all wanting to reach their destination. That power would be so great that any attempt to veer off the designated path would surely be challenged and guaranteed to crush you to death.

Nothing

He sleeps through the night. The minute his head hits the pillow means that's it until the morning. How can it be that he gets to sleep and sigh in deep pleasure, and I don't? Sometimes I try to wake him up because I get so mad at him for sleeping. I don't sleep very well. I cannot tell you really why that is. The doctor could find no reason for my insomnia. She said, you need to relax, you have an extremely busy mind. Quit thinking so much about everything. Then she turned away to open the door and called for her next patient. When I got home I researched Ten Zen Ideas for Bedrooms. Did you know the bedroom is the most important room in the house? Well, it transpires that positive energy or Qi was severely lacking in our bedroom. So I got him to move the bed around to face west instead of north. And I insisted the headboard hugged the wall. I hung a line of amethyst crystals in the window. But nothing worked. I kept getting mad at him for sleeping so well.

When he sleeps all night he wakes up refreshed and in a good mood. He will get out of bed to pull up the blind and start whistling some stupid tune over and over. His whistling makes me crazy. There are days when he gets back into bed and goes to touch me, and I get mad at that, too, because I'm too tired for sex. I tried to ask him not to sleep so well. I said that maybe if he didn't sleep so well, we could stay up and talk about stuff we needed to talk about. He said that's the worst excuse for staying up that he had ever heard of and rolled over and fell back asleep. Once I pinched him on the leg, and he woke up for a few seconds, rubbed the spot where I pinched him and then fell straight back asleep again. He didn't remember it in the morning because he never said anything about it. And the worst thing of all is that he has the most fantastic dreams that he can recount in detail. That's something considering he can never find his keys.

What's Wrong with You?

...And he would ask me what's wrong with you while shaking his head in disgust. What about all that you have? A husband, a car, a vegetable garden, a cat, fresh flowers in a vase, a dog, good food, a fireplace, framed paintings on the wall, a doorbell, expensive face cream, velvet skirts, waxed legs, an exercise regime, a collection of poetry books, bookshelves made from cherry wood, copper-based saucepans, French perfume to spray on your skin, clean bathrooms, a few heirlooms, a linen closet, tiled floors, a bureau, a lawn full of daffodils in the spring, fluffy white towels, provocative conversation once a glass of wine is downed, regular appointments with the most expensive hair stylist in town and with your counsellor and the beauty technician, trips to the country hotel: lamb chops and turf fires, trips to that boutique hotel on the beach in the Costa Brava. What is bloody well wrong with you?

The Ending of the Days

I could easily picture myself standing outside the kitchen window looking in at the woman who was constantly searching for something she could never quite put her finger on but still felt uneasy that all was not quite right. Of course, Miss C. stood beside me, the only witness to the simple scene of a woman at a table with an unopened book before her, a cup of cold coffee in a chipped cup beside a bowl of slow-withering fruit and a blank page the woman thought about filling but never did.

The woman at the table wore glass earrings the colour of new green peas and her husband's plaid dressing gown. It really could have been a painting titled, *Dawn Table, Unopened Book, a Cup of Coffee, a Bowl of Slow-Withering Fruit and a Blank Page*. The woman at the table thought about everything even though it seemed to her at the time her mind was on nothing much all at once. She mused over money and vistas of skies and what to make for dinner and the baking of cakes and desiring sex or not desiring sex, and why the snails wedged to the patio wall caused her to ponder on their very existence. She thought the snails seemed stuck mid-way, wondered if the snails' shells were heavy or if it merely depended on how efficiently the snails carried them. The woman liked to think of the snails eventually reaching the longed-for luxury of the borage leaves where, basking unhindered in the sweet undergrowth, they could have time to plan a new course.

The woman at the table didn't know it then, but those days had become the before of the ending days. She rose early in the hope that she could find what she was looking for. She wished she could fill in the blank page with its sea blue lines. She tried, but the ink turned to blotches of disconnected letters before she could even form a simple sentence. It was like learning to write all over again, the struggle with the first grasp of a pen alien in your hands as you attempt to connect the curls and strands of vowels and consonants together to form a coherent sentence, only to find to your frustration that no matter how hard you try, the letters hang limp and broken, without any hope of finding a home. Think of a t without the cross or the i with the little dot missing on top, or the many doors of rooms left half unlocked where the openings are way too narrow to enter. Filling lines is the same as trying to figure why people come and go. How they can hug and love you one day, and the next be gone with only half a shadow remaining. A mere filament of memory like the splendour of coming upon a blossoming flower one day and the next when you go back out to admire it in the garden, you discover you merely covet it more when it is no longer there.

Crumbs

On the next scheduled day, exactly two weeks after our initial rendezvous, I repeated the previous steps to meet Dr. J. I took the express train to the town where nobody knew him, to the hotel by the river that was quite impersonal, to room three-four-three where I knocked three times before he let me in. The stale air that previously clawed the room was no longer there. I guessed Dr. J. had called for a janitor to come fix the window because it was wide open, and the curtains billowed innocently in a light breeze. I stood on the crappy floral carpet and waited for him to speak. He was finishing a sandwich, and I resisted the urge to brush some crumbs like small brown pebbles off his sweater. He told me to make myself comfortable. Today, he said, would be a good idea to remove my upper garments and then to go lie down on the bed as before. He said he was anxious to start because he had to be back in his office for an important conference call. Nevertheless, he was quick to insist that an hour would be more than sufficient for the purpose of the study and that I should not rush but remove my clothes slowly. Yes, there you go, he said, raise your wonderful arms and pull that jumper up over your head and then unbutton your blouse, each button an occasion. The colour suits you, by the way; coral, he said, is becoming, always a good choice for your skin tone. Now to the bra, he said, black and lacy and a little bold, and he tapped his professorial lips with his lily-white hands. Maybe, he added with a little chuckle thrown in for good measure, I mean, you are no spring chicken. Interesting choice, though. I want you now to touch your breasts briefly. Yes, do it playfully and momentarily as if it is purely an afterthought. I did as I was told and felt a tingling between my legs. I drew my breath in and let it out slowly. I felt as if I could come without even trying. Now, let us not get too carried away here, he said, sensing my arousal, we are verbally copulating, don't you remember? We must stick to the rules. It is not easy to recall much more about that visit. I know he spoke about how special it was to have me in the room with him and how he enjoyed looking at me lying semi-naked on the bed. He asked me how I felt, and I said, new and special, but I only said that because I figured that was what he wanted to hear me say. By then he had removed his shirt, and I wished he hadn't because his stomach rested in flabby layers like pink sausages lined up in a row. I thought of a little pig grunting in a filthy pen and wondered what the hell I was doing in room three-four-three in a town where nobody knew him, in a dump of a hotel by a stagnant river that was quite impersonal. And as I puzzled over these things, he rambled on about copulation and masturbation and alienation and vibration and differentiation and citations and all the other bloody 'ations' in a room by a river where I knew was definitely, definitively, the ending of something that never quite had a chance to properly begin.

Plain or Purl?

To date, having written all of these words, I can accept that many may appear a little off kilter, like a badly proportioned room where the doorway is too small and the windows way too big and everything else in between is either unbalanced or out of focus. It's as if the room is all part of a weird, disjointed dream. Yes, I am quite agreeable to that, and I take the blame for this. However, let me stress that the construction of a story is a most challenging task and therefore, not doing a good job of it is highly probable. If you forget the room analogy for a moment and if you happen to undertake a spot of knitting now and then, you will be able to imagine a process of mixing up the stitches by knitting too many purls or too many plains or vice versa by not knitting nearly enough purls and not enough plains. But while I set out to try to explain myself and Miss C., I believe the somewhat truncated process needs to be as organic as possible for the story to be credible. Even so, it is easy to locate the finger pointers who will gladly accuse me of all kinds of things like dropped stitches I either failed to see or chose to ignore or to dismiss and continued to knit to the point where it can be too late to retrieve the stitches knowing there is no hope in hell that I am about to unravel back through those damn complicated and often times dropped stitches to try to reform my story into a more coherent pattern. No. I must proceed because it has taken me this amount of time to arrive here, to this stage, meaning hours and hours agonising over my desk in the early hours, gulping down cold coffee from blue mugs, agonising over my desk, yes, I am aware that I said that already and I'll say it again,

agonising over the desk in my mind,

in my... memory,

in my... I'd rather not go in that room,

in my... I am quite sure that I do not have to go into that room,

in my... that room is way too cold to be sitting in,

in my... that room certainly doesn't like me,

in my... that room stinks,

in my... why is that room calling out my name,

in my... I'd rather not, thank you very much room,

...and all the while Miss C. patiently waited on the sidelines, counting to the end, trying to hinder me from unravelling the wool, suggesting I follow the pattern, knowing it would in time reveal all, but still she was clever enough to ask me what on earth a baggy sweater with dropped stitches was doing in this scenario and most importantly pretending to guess what the finished product would look like even when the final stitch had been perfectly purled.

American Beauty

I've decided it is best if I limit myself to the quiet rooms these days. Even though I admit, even before now, there were times when I also sought out the quietude of certain rooms. Even then they allowed a form of escape, to become a refuge of sorts and a place to rest my weary head. Ah, the quiet room beckoned when my broken brain needed to regenerate. There I'd be heading up the stairs trying not to make a sound by lightly tipping and toeing along the passageway, careful to avoid the creaks and squeaks of the old busy body tell-tale floorboards. Step by dainty step, barefoot, taking my time. The little broken girlie looking to get away from it all and her not knowing why. Why does a broken brain need a break? Nobody says why. Instead they say you are fine. You survived the worst. Go on. Go on. So you go to lie on the bed and study the ceiling. Follow the cracks overhead, some connected, some not, some trying to be cracks but not quite becoming cracks. Yet.

When the light through the window begins to fade, you reach out to turn on a small bedside lamp and begin to make silly little shapes with your hands to reflect on the wall. Shadows are my friends. A big-eared bunny rabbit and a talking duck that goes yakety-yak. You laugh away to yourself. Like a private snigger session. Fun having this rapport with a room. Nobody need ever know. You're thinking how much you love this quiet room, this sanctuary. Lift up a book and turn the pages. Listen to the soft whisper of paper turning before you. Close your eyes. Your life feels like it will go on forever and forever and forever. You cannot imagine how long it will be. Then this happens. Don't fool yourself into thinking otherwise that this quiet house full of quiet rooms won't happen. This woman creeping past the rooms listening for any inkling of a sound. Wanting a sound. Any damn sound.

What was it again? What did he say again? Something about a woman. A new client. She came to him with a problem. Actually he emphasized, lots of problems. That's how he brought it up. A young adult, he said. Not a really so young adult. I mean, really? Maybe an almost forty-something young adult, he said. Well, that's young now, isn't it, I said to Miss C., who stifled a laugh and raised her eyes to heaven. She came into his office, he said, the office I helped him set up. Actually, the office I set up while he wrote his papers, books, his undisputed opinions. I was the one who went out to the office furniture supply stores on the outskirts of this city and trudged around the endlessly cold grey functional steely aisles for several days before I finally found the desk. Yes, a circular desk was definitely more modern, more in keeping with his inclusive technique, with the times that were in it and the current trend, and besides, rectangles were beyond passé in all of the who's who interiors. Let's go for white walls and a white floor, I said. White birch, actually. Renowned for its beauty and durability. Cool yet soft to practically engage with the client. And allow me to mention the essential mature ficus tree for the corner near the sliding doors and how it exudes a certain sense of optimism. Of course we made sure the tall blonde bookshelves were well stacked with self-help books and dishevelled journals and reference books. Check. And we certainly cannot forget the dozen or so books he'd authored or coauthored that deserved a shelf all to themselves. Check. And let us not forget the suitable piles of current magazines, including *Home and Rooms*, of course, casually strewn on the glass-topped coffee table in the waiting area. Check. And finally a water cooler with high mountain spring, extra pure water on tap, worth the extra cost, delivered on a weekly basis. Check.

And in all of this deliberate exposé, let us not forget me, his loyal and exquisite assistant, at the ready twenty-four seven, with notebook in hand, ready and alert in his consulting room, pen eager for note taking, listening for instructions, cleaning the stinking toilets, polishing his circular desk with specially imported bees wax, standing in his consulting room tending to his needs, when for the first time, he reveals something, tells me straight up without any hesitation that the almost forty something young woman, yes his client, actually smelled of spring flowers. He said it as if he were making an innocent observation, like it was no big deal. He said it as if he might have been commenting on the rose bushes bound to the ancient patio walls. He said it as if in passing, just as he said he noticed for the very first time in twenty-eight years that the American Beauty lasts for such a brief time, possibly only a full month from the initial bloom until the blooms begin to fade and disintegrate into something resembling brittle brown cornflakes to become nothing again but green foliage and even that does not last. I hesitated then to ask him what the smell of spring flowers actually meant to him, but I eventually did. Of course I understood what the metaphor of spring flowers smelling actually means, but for him to describe somebody as smelling like spring flowers seemed so off-kilter, so distant from his usual pragmatic diagnostic theories, that I was immediately curious as to what the smelling like spring flowers meant to him. He said after some moments that spring flowers smell like youth and promise and vitality, and as he said it he stood at the long windows where he laid both his hands on the glass like he was bracing himself to say something formidable and that he had anticipated my question before I'd even asked him what a spring flower smell is like. I said that's nice. He said, yes, I'm afraid she will have to come back again, that the consultation was not concluded; it was more complicated, he said. I said again, oh, that's nice. Then he turned to me and brushed his hand lightly on my arm, hesitating at my side as if to suggest something more before quickly dismissing it by saying he had work to do. He left me then to go to sit in his big leather chair at his circular desk.

Some days later I watched the woman who smelled like spring flowers get out of her fire-engine red mini car to follow the walkway scented by the rapidly decaying American Beauties to his consulting room for her scheduled appointment. I wondered would she rifle distractedly through a recent *New Yorker* magazine while she waited in the waiting area. Thumbing the page to read a poem or a restaurant review. But that scenario seemed like a thought that really didn't matter. I saw that she looked very young and most likely someone who never spent too much time noticing or thinking about rooms of any kind the way I did. Her hair was long and straw blonde, and she wore a lot of makeup and gold jewellery so that she sparkled like a trinket, a souvenir of something useless but pretty one might hang from the rearview mirror of a car. I believed then that it was to be the beginning of quiet rooms for me. Rooms I did not necessarily seek out but, as yet, I did not know that all rooms were to be this way from then on, whether I cared to accept it or not. They were to become a prison sentence of a kind. Like I was to be in permanent confinement in a house full of solitary rooms, where all the cracks on the ceiling had eventually connected and, in the chaos of the crazy design, began to make sense. I was perhaps to finally solve a challenging puzzle I never could have figured out until I had the sense to stand back to allow nature to take its course. It was then that I saw how the intricate designs of the cracks on the ceilings kept me busy for a long time. You see cracks on the ceiling reveal so much more than first meets the eye. It takes a long time to even dare to accept that the cracks finally have nowhere else to go but to backtrack the way they came and try to reconnect if possible. But that kind of thinking is merely a naive type of optimism and not at all a reality.

Time

Nights are all the same now. I turn off the television, ensure the curtains are fully drawn, put the dog out and wait for her to come back in again before I head up the stairs. It crosses my mind for the first time that my movement has changed. Slightly slower, no, no, not that, but I'm more cautious with my left hand clamped to the banister for support. In the bedroom I see him sitting on the edge of the bed, carefully removing his wristwatch in that studied, methodical way he has perfected. First the strap has to be slowly released from its clasp, then once off his wrist, the leather is ironed out before the precision is confirmed, allowing the watch to be wound, and after that he places it facedown like a treasured artefact on the bedside dresser. At exactly ten p.m. he fluffs up his pillows four times with tender, playful punches, switches off the lamp and allows sleep to carry him away. I undress in the bathroom. Perfectly composed, I will don my nightgown, rub night cream into my wrinkling skin, floss and brush my teeth, swirling and swishing the minty mouthwash down the plughole. Some nights it comes to me that the yesterday doors have finally caught up with the tomorrow doors I had so looked forward to and how soon they would meld into each other with nothing more to follow. Absolutely nothing.

Room Type

I'd often remark to the one who shall not be named how I felt sure the rooms had a certain way of taking hold of one. I was positive it had to do with how they are, quite understandably, the metaphorical blotting paper soaking us up whether we want it to or not. Think about it; rooms are really where the residue we unknowingly discard throughout every tiny second of our existence ends up. Just imagine the zillion little bits of skin that flake off our bodies as we reach out to, say, scratch an itchy back or wipe away that nasty sneeze we desperately attempt to control but can't, or those shameful tears that trickle hotly down our cheeks. Well, dummies, guess what? Those invisible parts that I'm talking about eventually land on the walls of the rooms we inhabit and build over time layer upon invisible layer. And while I'm on the subject, where do you think all the words we dare to utter go? Ha ha ha, you should have seen Miss C.'s face when I went on like that. She looked amazed at my revelations. But really, I mean, what was she thinking? That everything just disappears into outer space? What I'm trying to say (in my matter-of-fact voice) is that rooms take on a personality fitting to themselves and, just like people, there are airy rooms, formal rooms, gloomy cranky rooms, happy rooms, confused rooms, orderly rooms, neat and tidy rooms, angry rooms, shy rooms, exclusive rooms, ordinary rooms, pensive rooms, messy rooms, idyllic rooms, mellow rooms, envious rooms... so you see if there is too much grief in one room, well then that room is going to be the saddest most miserable damn room in the entire world, and no matter how one tries to throw in an occasional laugh or crack a joke out loud, there is no hope in hell this room will ever change its personality. In simple terms, that room, the saddest, most miserable damn room in the entire world, will resist any attempts on your part to change it. Therefore the cheerfulness desired will never penetrate grief. It always wins over, and anything else will be resisted at all costs. That last sentence was, as I recall, uttered aloud to drive home to Miss C. the seriousness of these pressing matters.

Sorrow

When did all the tomorrows become yesterdays? Was it around the time when the rooms started to fade and blur until they eventually bled together to form an endless narrative that kept spinning around in my head? When did I want to scream stop at him and at myself? I knew he was worried about what people would think of me. Okay. So he was concerned one afternoon upon discovering me leaning over the kitchen countertop wearing nothing but a string of beads. I was talking to my tree outside the window. Yes. You heard right. I was having a conversation with my ash tree. Besides, he wasn't expected home for at least a few hours. And if you really want to know, it was just something I did now and then when the coast was clear. It didn't hurt anyone, and it made me feel good, and the tree understood that, considering how we had grown together over the years. The long, seemingly endless years when I stood in the kitchen baking and cooking and ironing and looking out at my tree smiling in at me. Why sometimes I'd sense her bending gracefully towards me so that she could listen to my songs and my woes. I loved that tree in every season, but come autumn, when she blew herself about the place preparing for her winter's sleep, well, that was my favourite time of all.

One day in late October when the last of the leaves had tumbled from her limbs, he told me her roots were bad news. Actually, he didn't use the word bad. He said, lethal. He said to avoid big trouble ahead, we needed to take action before the roots spread so deep and far beneath the ground that we would have a branch sticking right up through the kitchen floor. He said it like it was the end of the world. As he talked, I imagined my tree reaching out, wanting to join me in the house, to sit beside us at the table, share in the conversation, problem-solve the polar bears, fix global warming. Apologies, I digress. Still, this is the truth: the bottom line, the tree had to go. So, he called up the tree company. He was good at that. Calling up people to solve problems. The tree company guy arrived the very next day to look at the tree and to give a quote. Is it that vital to know how much it is to murder a tree? I didn't want to know. But there he was out in the garden with the tree company guy chatting like old buddies reunited, dancing in and out of each other around the tree. The tree company guy in a high vis jacket and hard hat casually ran his big dirty red mottled hands along the branches, as if he might have been contemplating how he would make love to it, before he leaned beneath her and touched the bark, tap tapping it over and over to find any weak spots. Then he stood back to consider the verdict, to perform the nod of death; the deed is done kind of nod, and effusive, manly handshakes followed to seal the deal.

I was out doing errands when the tree company guy sent his worker to the house. He used a big angry yellow chainsaw to murder my tree. When I got home I walked by the worker with the raucous, angry yellow chainsaw. He kept revving it up like a threat that would never end. The long and graceful limbs made me think of an amputated ballet dancer strewn about on the lawn. In the kitchen I stood at my usual place by the countertop, and when I looked out the window, I could see nothing, only grey sky. I closed the blind and waited for silence.

Has He, Has He, Has He?

And a brief interlude to clarify some pressing matters. Let's call it a little Q&A shall we?

Has he, of late, attempted to touch you or demonstrate any affection towards you?

No, he has not.

Has he looked at you from across the kitchen table for no reason whatsoever?

No, he has not.

Has he asked how you are feeling?

No, he has not.

Has he, at least recently, ran his fingers along your back while you lie beside him first thing on waking?

No, he definitely has not.

Has he, in the last few years, ever once suggested you both go away for a night to stay in that special hotel by the coast?

No, he has not.

And in the past ten years has he dared to put his hand between your legs and feel for the wetness and put his fingers to his nostrils in order to relish your scent?

No, never.

Incy Wincy Spider

The thing about spiders is that in their stealthy way of exist-
ing, one actually never knows if they're watching you, possibly getting ready to bite or if, at the very least, they move a
little bit closer to you to get a better look. Let us not forget
that poor woman who was unaware of the spider who lived
in her ear and that, that same spider had, so to speak, set up
shop by crawling in one unexceptional day in a most quiet and
unobtrusive respectable way, steadily moving nicely along the
woman's arm while she most likely sat reading a book in a cosy
room oblivious to the clever spider who, having rested briefly
on the woman's shoulder took the final ascent across her glorious hair to one of her dainty ears where it leapt lightly into
the cavernous ear canal to immediately sigh in deep approval
upon seeing the soft pink walls within, the ambient tempera-
ture and the low lighting most conducive to sleep. An added
bonus came with the joyous realisation that there were no
other spiders in the vicinity, and so with these ideal factors
in place, the clever spider curled itself up to settle down for a
long nap. The woman, thinking she had water in her ear, went
to her doctor, who extracted the sleeping spider and clumsily
allowed it to scurry beneath a gap in the skirting board to plot
its next victim.

If only I could do that. Become a spider for a day. I'd set up
shop in his lover's ear and patiently bide my time for him to
come. While lying in his lover's ear, I'd hear her go about her
business. She would shower in preparation for his visit, softly

soaping her white body with bergamot and lilies, singing a little tune, sad and hopeful at the same time. She would be drying her skin with a big white fluffy towel, vigorously mussing up her hair to ensure her blonde curls would be more vibrant just for him. She would be smoothing lotions scented with spring flowers and marshmallows all over her body, down between her legs, behind her ears and riffling through a drawer, she would choose a lacy top and matching panties the colour of coal. She would be running a ruby red lipstick carefully across her generous lips, making little smacking sounds afterwards. And on hearing the delicate ping of the doorbell, she'd be hurrying down the stairs. He'd come in and place his jacket on the coat stand in the hallway as naturally as if he had come home. He'd be kissing her. Saying oh, my god, you are amazing as he followed her upstairs, shedding his clothes along the way until he stood naked in the room with the honey gold velvet curtains quickly unleashed from their tasselled state. He'd be kissing her gently then, down below between her legs, saying how he wants to fuck her. How he can't wait. He'd be fucking her then, and when the room finally fell quiet, I would unfold my long spidery legs and make my way out into the darkness, turning once to see his hands lost in her tangled hair.

The Allocator

I was completely taken aback when I saw how he appeared to be in total agreement with the Homeless-Room-Allocation-Inspector, who having arrived precisely at the appointed time, looked exactly how I'd imagined a Homeless-Room-Allocation-Inspector would look, dressed in his distinguished smart black uniform and a pert red cap that said Allocator across the peak in bright yellow lettering. He carried in his stout little arms an official-looking black folder designed in the shape of a house, complete with a pointed rooftop and cutouts of windows and doors clearly meant to represent an ethos of inclusivity. He, my most welcoming and law-abiding spouse, said, to the Homeless-Room-Allocation-Inspector, in no hesitant terms whatsoever, how yes, it was indeed our civic duty to share our glorious rooms with those less fortunate folk. He said this while tenderly caressing one of his prized tomes as he sat on the couch alongside the Homeless-Room-Allocation-Inspector, who made frequent notations and cheeky ticks on the pages in his black folder shaped like a house. And while this feigned camaraderie ensued, I was figuring out what my gracious, welcoming spouse was thinking. I was thinking, am I really thinking what I am thinking? I was thinking that he thinks this will be a great distraction. And that this designated individual, this homeless person allocated to our home, would be a welcome project, useful in keeping me from (wink, wink) snooping around in his affairs. And guess what? For once Miss C. didn't dare to disagree with me.

Reflection

And then that day arrives. The day you never once stopped to consider, when seemingly out of nowhere loneliness comes calling at the door. In my case it happens when I'm sitting on that old bench by the kitchen table minding my own business, when I'll suddenly realise I long for a visitor imagining what it might be like. How they would arrive with some flowers or a small box of carefully chosen, mouth-watering petit fours, fresh from the French bakery in town. My guests admitting how they decided to visit me purely on the likelihood that they would find me home. Me nodding along with them, lilting aloud how I absolutely love spontaneity in people. It's a dying art these days, don't you agree, I'd say laughingly.

We know what a busy life you lead, they'd stress, so we are thrilled, simply thrilled, to find you here in your beautiful home.

Of course I'd invite them in. Of course with a flurry to arrange the delicate cakes on my favourite blue plate and put the kettle on to make some tea. I'd even resurrect the old china teapot. Why not? Make an occasion of it. The good cups too. And I would tell Miss C. to put a lid on her whispering and funny faces for a start. Tell her I am bloody tired of her goings on. Tell her to leave me be so I can concentrate on my entertaining. Oh, how I love that heavenly sound of silver spoons settling themselves onto a tea tray. When the tea is brewed, I'd casually invite my guests to sit in the dining room at the long table, and there would be so much to say that the time, well, I, I'd never notice it passing. And I might even make a second pot of tea, allowing it to draw for at least ten minutes because they said it was so good. Real tea leaves, I'd insist, make all the difference. And when they stand reluctantly to leave, they might say something like what if we do this again soon. Finally, after bidding them goodbye, that long absent feeling of exhilaration hits me like a fast-acting tonic. So pleased with my life, I might even venture outside to pick some yellow flowers from the end of the garden before the day begins to close in a most agreeable way believing I feel I am somebody for the first time in months.

But there is no one at the doorbell, and even the street is empty of passersby as far as that goes, and the only sound is the clock ticking in the kitchen. As I go to walk around the house, I see how the windscreen of my car, parked out on the driveway, is reflected onto the wall in the hall, and it frames an unusually bright light that makes the reflection look real, like a mirror, and I notice that if I stand, yes, if I stand in the doorway with my back to the sun, my entire form is then reflected onto that magical mirror. I can actually see myself from behind. I could be another person standing behind me, looking at me. And it shows up everything. And it's saying, look at that lonely woman stripped of everything. Nothing else. It says you are a nothing middle-aged woman stranded in a doorway who doesn't know if she is coming or going. Why I begin to take off my clothes, I do not know. But there is something so deeply satisfying about standing half naked in a doorway with the late afternoon sunlight warming your back. I stand there until I begin to see myself for the very first time.

Who's There?

Knock, knock, who's there?

Miss C.

Miss C. who?

Miss C. and me.

Me and Miss C.

Hee, hee, hee.

Our Well-Behaved Rooms

So each day we went about our everyday ways, our private, separate ways, in our well-behaved rooms on ordinary days, on so-very-agreeable days, on so-what-would-people-think kind of days, on so-please-pass-the-butter kind of days, on so-is-that-the-car-insurance-bill days, on so-are-we-out-of-Scotch tape days, on so-isn't-the-weather-terrible days, on so-I-think-the-toaster-is-broken days, on so many ordinary days that sometimes when meeting as we would in passing, he en route to his office and me trying to find something to do with my mind, my days, I thought we might as well have been co-workers who upon meeting at the water cooler choose to exchange some light-hearted pleasantries about the weather or the state of the nation or the price of coffee beans, and yet once the co-worker was out of earshot the other co-worker curses her co-worker and speaks badly about him. Yes, because the truth is I knew, alright. I knew because he had a fresh fidgety way about him. I knew because he wore brand new twill shirts in blues and pinks. I must admit the colours were much more becoming than the drab black he went for before. I knew he knew I knew that he was still having a little something, a little dessert, so to speak, on the side. And is it a shame to admit that I was possibly relieved? That I was pleased to be left alone? Or was I angry and sullen and lonely? To be honest, it was a little bit of both. I either despised him for it or felt close to being thrilled at the very idea of it. Even a vague sense of him intimately touching another woman had, if I allowed it, an ability to arouse me. But please know that was only an occasional erring in my belief, so therefore, overall, I must reveal how once the co-worker was out of sight—

I hated him

I hated him

I hated him.

Opt for the Minimum

Miss C. was happy to remind me how, when all was said and done, we did not really have a say in the matter because it was never even presented as anything that would be remotely optional. You see, I'm referring to the new law enacted, where all homeowners with rooms to spare were without delay required to let out said rooms to the nation's rapidly growing number of homeless citizens. It was an option for many years, but matters were to quickly change. This is how the Homeless-Room-Allocation-Inspector presented it to us: we could either avail of the early 'let the room out now' scheme that required a minimum tenancy contract of one person, or in a very short time after that, those who governed us stated we would not have a choice on the number of tenants and, as a result, would have to agree, that's what it said, agree to, all of the unused rooms in one's house becoming available to the less well-off individuals in society. Obviously there is no prize for guessing we opted for the minimum tenancy requirement, although I was certain even that agreement, in time, might be challenged and the number of tenants increased. Therefore it wasn't at all difficult to picture hordes of homeless strangers equipped with their own keys, coming in and out of the house at ungodly hours to happily traipse around my orderly and neatly catalogued rooms as if they rightfully belonged to them. I mean to say it wasn't in the slightest bit difficult to imagine these unsavoury characters padding about in bare feet or in threadbare socks, clad in shorts and vests, going to stand by the fire while rubbing their backsides to warm themselves up and humming endlessly or whistling irritatingly repetitive and senseless tunes as they ambled over to the bread basket to help themselves to our bread, to put slices of our bread into our toaster and to reach for our marmalade and call out to no one in particular, if there was any more butter, unsalted if you please, and, and then afterwards, before throwing themselves down on one of our fabulous antique upholstered couches to read, would peruse the bookshelves for the most treasured of books, the ones I didn't even permit the children to borrow never mind these unwelcome unsavoury scoundrels.

Truly this is how the future looked to me back then. The future consisted of a bunch of straggly strangers queuing up to move in. I have to say, it was challenging trying to pretend to be kind and not to think of those people, of those homeless human beings, as criminals, layabouts, rapists, thieves, drunks and racketeers all waiting to lay claim to my rooms.

Reprieve

There were days, albeit few, when reprieve came politely calling at the back door, early mornings, usually summertime. This was, I hasten to add, long before the city conquered this place as it has now. You would understand if you had seen me back then tripping lightly down the stairs. I can confidently say that I was full of gleeful anticipation for the day ahead. In the kitchen, I'd turn the faucet to fill the yet untarnished kettle and wait for the smooth promise of its whistle. Then pulling up the blind, I would witness, to my delight, two cows grazing in the yellow meadow beyond. One brown, one white, I thought of a painting: *Beasts at Dawn.* So rapt was I with what was in my vision that I would go leaning forward against the windowpane before digging out my boots and carefully lifting the back door latch to go down across the dewy drenched grass, singing a small song to carry me along through the gap in the fuchsia hedge, gaily dressed in silver gossamer threads glittering in the new light. It was easy going up and over the rickety old fence to the place where the beasts stood still as statues in faraway galleries. Down on my knees, I'd crawl through the scrub and the stones, the sweetest of heather honey on my tongue, and the juiciest berries, black as night, hanging from my lobes. When I spoke to the beasts, it was in an alien voice like a crooning, crooning, crooning. A comfort sound from someplace deep within me, a pledge of peace of sorts to show I was only there seeking solidarity. Reaching out to touch their smooth, warm, pliant udders, the drool from shiny black nostrils was a salve to cool my skin and ward off all of what had frightened me. But my temporary reprieve always assured me the same ending with those voices calling me from far off across the field, urging me, with a sense of panic in their voices, to return immediately as they threatened how time was nigh before it got to be too late and the door to the room would be shut forever.

Our House Is Your House

Tenant 156 stood at the front door. He reminded me of a dog waiting to be allowed in because he knew his master had already prepared his food, and as soon as the door opened, he could hurry in, panting and wagging his tail before heading straight to the bowl of food on the floor and, without hesitating, begin to eat his delicious meal.

That day I saw Tenant 156 place a small suitcase, the size of a carry-on suitcase, carefully on the stoop and place what I now know to be his saxophone case on the other side. Then he lifted his long, elegant fingers to smooth his greying hair with dampened palms before straightening his tie. He might as well have been applying the finishing touches to his outfit before an important job interview or audition at Carnegie Hall. I waited in the living room trying to decide if, on his arrival, I should offer him some coffee or if I should immediately direct him, in a businesslike way with only necessary small talk, to his room on the other side of the house where we had, many years ago, rearranged a room for the children's entertainment. Clearly I wished the day had never come, that I felt sure I would most likely lose my mind and that I was more than resentful. All in all, I decided I had little to say to him apart from:

Welcome, Tenant 156, to our home,

Our house is your house—

Your own home sweet home—

Because there's no place like home now, is there—

Because we all happen to know how home is where the heart is—

Now this is to become your home away from home—

And come on now, relax, home is not a place but a feeling—

And here you are because, Tenant 156, we all believe that taking the best journey takes you home here.

And then I went to welcome Tenant 156, who most likely was anxiously awaiting the freedom of my home, who stood at the entrance waiting to become part of the home, our home, our bloody home, our bloody fucking empty home, our home with all the rooms tidied and neat and untouched, our home where he was unwelcome, our home where the ghosts could appear at any moment to begin their mocking chant, to niggle its way into my ears and into this home full of empty promises and so, Tenant 156, now please, now please wipe your shoes on the mat, and remember on wet days you must remove them before proceeding further, and I will remind you there will be no smoking on the premises or in the garden and please, please respect the privacy of others, and I went to answer the doorbell not knowing what I would actually say to Tenant 156 as I turned the lock to allow him to come in out of the rain.

I Backstab, You Backstab

I knew he was up to something

I knew he was up to something

I knew he was up to something

. . .

He knew I knew

He knew I knew

He knew I knew

. . .

But we never let on

But we never let on

But we never let on

. . .

Because it suited us in a way

Because it suited us in a way

Because it suited us in a way

.   .   .

It was a mutual agreement

It was a mutual agreement

It was a mutual agreement

.   .   .

Homecoming

I'm reconstructing here. I'm aware of how I've already written
about Tenant 156 ringing the doorbell, and I'll say it again. The
doorbell rang only once. It was a gentle, considered ring and
not a demanding urgent peal. No, there was absolutely no indication of a digit being impatiently pressed on the small white
illuminated button for longer than was necessary. Instead the
ring came from someone who might have had the sensitivity
to know that it is good manners to press a doorbell once and
only once, so by the time I arrived at the door to open it, I had
already gone from being resentful to being resigned to being
resentful so many times over, that as I prepared to greet the
caller, I did not actually know how my greeting mode would
appear. Although it did occur to me that the ring, that gentle single doorbell ring, was saying no hurry, please take your
time, touch up your lipstick, dispel any doubts that are beginning to resurface, pleading for your attention and with that in
mind I walked slowly down the hallway and faced the door
to stand for a moment before I raised my hand to the latch
and unbolted the lock to allow him to step inside. And as I did
this, all in slow motion, of course, I raised my arm, heavy with
suppressed negativity, to undo the bolt that snapped open like
the cork of a champagne bottle, and there he was with his
eager outstretched hand, his long lovely cold hand for me to
take into my hand, for the palms to connect, for the dermis
to make shy love on the doorstep and so I put out my hand,
my small hot hand to his because that is what you do and he
stepped in, lifting one foot, then the other like a perfectly cal-

ibrated windy-up toy and we, Miss C. and I, could see how his face was open like a new day in spring after a long winter of only darkness and gloom, and he said without saying it aloud, now this is nice. And the hallway listened, and the rooms leaned forward to eavesdrop, and the shadows whispered 'whist' as they waited for a sign of some sort apart from the sharp cold air that wafted through the open doorway as Tenant 156 lifted his suitcase and his saxophone case through the frame. Then another painting came to me, titled – *Man Standing in Doorway Having Returned from a Long Trip Abroad, as Woman, Dressed in a Sapphire Blue Dress with a Scarlet Butterfly Pinned to Her Hair, Welcomes Him Home.*

Strangers in the Night

Sleepless nights cast thoughts in and out of the black river in my head as he schemes his next well-constructed move that certainly has to do with my demise. And I listen to the night how it simply is – the great stretch of night minding its own business and how I can't escape the big bloodshot-eyed beast lurking in the closets and beneath the bed, ready to jump out if I let go of the covers or if I dare open my mouth to say:

I'm scared.

Hold me.

Talk to me like you used to.

Scratch my back.

Do you hear the monsters in here too?

Tell me what the rumbling is about.

Tell me everything will be okay.

Do you still feel something for me?

If you could be anywhere else right now, where would it be?

Will I tell you a story about Johnny Magory?

Will I begin it?

That's all that's in it.

What's the capital of Liberia?

Ha, ha, got you.

Can you feel Tenant 156 in this house?

You recite a poem.

I'll recite a poem.

What will we have for dinner tomorrow?

What's your dream vacation?

Is red still your favourite colour?

Why don't you believe in God?

Is climate change real?

Can you tell me something you've never told anyone?

Why don't you ever touch me?

But I never said any of that.

No. Instead, I counted all of his inhalations and all of his exhalations, noting how his exhalations were greater than his inhalations as if he had far more to confide to the night.

A Thing of Beauty

I tried to make sense of how I felt that first time. I actually couldn't tell if it was the way the room suited him or the way he suited the room. But when a tiny inkling of enlightenment flitted through my brain, it occurred to me that something can become more beautiful when it is struck by some kind of imperfection. I explained this point to Miss C., suggesting how if a blue teacup happens to be missing its handle, then said blue teacup becomes more unique than it was before the handle broke off, and bear with me, but have you ever noticed how an eye with a slight cast draws you in much more than say a bright twinkling dancing eye, and look at how a scar, a small and barely discernible scar becomes something of wonder and mystery when discovered, almost like coming upon a tiny lake in an endless landscape of infertile deserts. Well, that's how it was the day Tenant 156 stood in the snowy bright room, the minimalistic, neutral room designated to him, that yes, at that very moment, he did appear to me as a thing of beauty. Yes, Tenant 156 looked beautiful that day, as if he finally landed on the shore after a long voyage and was trying to decide if it had been worth the journey or if the destination was just another room, temporary and charitable, or did it cross his mind that perhaps he had come home at last as he sat on the bed to test the mattress and stand up again to limp across to the window where he stood looking out at the copse of sumac trees beginning to turn. When he turned to me and said, I am v-very p-pleased to m-meet you and th-thank y-you, th-thank y-you f-for th-this... well I had already left the room to return to our living quarters, our perfect rooms, our dearest most empty lonely rooms on the other side of the house where I knew he'd be waiting for me trying to decide on whether he was coming or whether he was going.

Ruminations

For all of those days in all of those rooms, I wasn't left with very much to show for it. It was, in a way, akin to relishing the idea of a long soak in the bathtub, and having gone to fill it, I was, all along, unaware that the stopper wasn't properly in the drain hole so that as soon as the water entered the tub, it immediately drained back out again because when I turned around in that house, all I saw was a bunch of rooms that stared blankly back at me as if they never knew me at all. What happened? I do not know. I do recall asking him if he noticed how empty the rooms suddenly appeared, to which he replied, you need to do something now; explore what is left for you. I didn't like the implication in his words, being unwilling to admit my room ruminations had possibly been a waste of time. And besides, it was obvious he was only thinking about how he could keep me off his back.

Collide, Confuse, Coagulate and Conspire

Was it the way he held my eyes when he spoke to me? Was it his driftwood leg? Was it his seeming lack of expectation? Was it how he'd become homeless after an unfortunate accident? Was it how he appeared to have forgiven those who caused him to become homeless? Was it how he appeared humble and possibly shy when he told me how he'd lost everything and then looked around at the 'everything' of this house as if it really did not matter, did not count for anything? Was it how he was able to keep going despite adversity? Was it how it bothered me to see him depending on us to assist him? Was it about the time when I began to see myself in the picture? When I caught a glance of my frame just off stage, ready to appear when directed, and saw clearly how I had fallen for role of Victim? No, not immediately, this is true. No. Not overnight because Tenant 156 only revealed me to myself in a gradual way.

I recall telling Miss C. at the time to think of it as a little bit like watching a film. Let's call it *A Life Lived in Rooms*, where the first scene is a shot of a bedsit at the top of a ramshackle Georgian house somewhere in a big city. The young woman, a virgin, lives a solitary existence musing on the sky, going to bookstores, meeting older men who eventually get to have sex with her as the movie rolls on with scenes of rooms in various places, seasons, memories, people, innermost thoughts, hotel rooms, bedrooms, kitchens, all kinds of rooms, even mad rooms because she believes (is it her doing though?) that she is on a steady decline, a loss of reality into a place where the rooms are bound to collide, confuse, coagulate, conspire and collectively disintegrate with her in them and so by the time (let's not be hasty and give away the ending) the final scene in the movie appears, you are somewhat impressed with what you have seen so far that you remain seated to wait for the credits to appear, eager to see your name appear under Leading Cast Members, anticipating it will be beneath the category of leading female character, as in THE Leading Female Character. But the only indication of your appearance is way down the long list, actually quite a bit down the long list, where beside the list of inconsequential extras is a small-lettered notice stating: 'self-designated victim and complete and utter fraud'.

So basically the role assigned to Tenant 156 was to show me up. To call my bluff by silently and effectively saying, without any sugar coating whatsoever, what the fuck. He said, Christ, what's wrong with you?, as he surveyed the room and dragged his driftwood limb back and forth across the newly fitted double durable, carefully chosen Manhattan Grey laminate flooring before speaking haltingly as if practicing scales on his saxophone after not having played for some time, so the notes came out broken, hesitant and shrill when he eventually opened his mouth to say, I am v-very p-pleased to b-be h-here.

Sins

Bless me, Father, for I have sinned.

It's been forty-seven years since my last confession.

Father, before I tell you my sins, I would first like to comment on the decor of this confessing room. Suitably demure, Father, although (an aside here) do sins really require little or no lighting? I mean to say (and I interject as my qualifications happen to be in interior design), should sins not be high-lighted so we can all pay attention to them? Surely hiding them away in this claustrophobic space seems a tad unneces-sary. Don't you agree with me, Father?

Sorry, Father, but allow me to reiterate that I do happen to know something about rooms. I've made a study of them my entire life. If I'd had the good fortune or perhaps the foresight to have completed a doctorate, as my other half has so impres-sively achieved, my dissertation would have definitely been on rooms – titled, *A Life Lived in Rooms dot, dot, dot,* or possibly a more effective title would be: *How Rooms Impact Our Very Existence.*

I must say though, that this little confessing booth does main-tain that essential atmosphere required and so difficult to achieve nowadays. You could say it almost verges on drama and that it somehow lures the penance out of your bones, en-sures you repent whether you like it or not. Note the musty odour in the air, no doubt a result of the infusion of guilt emanating from the ornate oak carvings. Forgive me, Father, but I must remain seated (as I observe from your stance you do also) as my knees cannot tolerate pine anymore after years of bending and kneeling for other reasons, I might add. What did you say, Father? Speak up? Why am I here? Is that what you are asking me? I am here to confess. I am here to ask your forgiveness, dearest man clad in shiny stain-free cloth. You see, back when I was a child, I had a hard time coming up with sins. Why even one sin was impossible to locate. But I learnt quickly that sins are essential to get on the right side of God. How could I go to confession in a sinless state? Sins were my ticket to proceed. These are the sins I listed back then:

- I said a bad word
- I pinched my baby brother
- I ignored my mother when she called me
- I copied test answers from a girl at school
- I had bad thoughts about a teacher
- I thought about making up sins

We all have sin, don't we, Father? Isn't that right, Father? So go ahead, ask me now what are my sins today.

Tell me your sins, child.

I can't proceed, Father.

Proceed, child.

- I said a bad word, Father.

- I said. Fuck. Shit. Pussy. Cunt. Crap. Fucker. Shit head. Damn fucker.
- I thought about hate and sex with other people and..

I see, child.

- There are days when I do not like my husband, Father.
- Days when I look at him, and I think to myself, I don't like you.
- And some mornings I look at him and feel nothing at all about him.

I see, child.

- I get turned on thinking about him with another woman.

Bless you, child.

- Father, I haven't answered to God for what he has given me.
- I have pouted and scowled and allowed my nasty shadow to plant bad things in my ears. My shadow won.

I see, child. For your sins, my child (Father whispers), say ten forgiveness prayers and twenty-one guilt prayers. Amen.

A partition closes me off. It is a final and permanent farewell leaving in its wake a thin, uncertain light. A faint sound of a cassock brushes along the ancient floors to remind me of leaves dancing across a patio in autumn in a last-ditch attempt to harvest a final taste of summer. But apart from that brief perceived beautiful image, I see how this sin room devours my imperfections by belching and burping them up in serene satisfaction.

Profile

It would not be a lie when I say I seldom saw Tenant 156. He was able to come and go through a separate entrance to his living quarters. It seemed my fears were ill-founded about him taking over the house because he rarely appeared to make us aware of his existence, and I tended to imagine his very breath being invisible as if he had perfected a way to hush it up before it had a chance to form properly. But still I managed to figure him out, so to speak, by 'observing' him and by doing a little research of my own, and here is a small checklist applicable to him:

1. Real name Herbert Grouse (fact gleaned from scrunched-up envelope found in his room).
2. Adored anchovies (evidenced by the stack of empty tins neatly placed near garden bins).
3. Possessed a well-thumbed miniature illustrated book of Hopper paintings (always open on bedside table).
4. Gluten intolerant (clue: discarded bread wrapping).
5. Wore a 'Make our Planet Great Again' button on his overcoat (spotted hanging on coat stand).
6. Owned one CD (*Kind of Blue* by Miles Davis, left on shelf).

I can also report that our Herbert Grouse, aka Tenant 156, found a job, part-time, (possibly due to him having an address, our address) in a jazz bar on the other side of town. I can say the jazz place allowed him to go there during the day, enabling him to play his beloved saxophone and thereby ensuring he did not disturb anyone in his allocated place of residence.

You see, I can personally vouch for all of the above because Miss C. and I, unbeknownst to one H. Grouse, followed him one afternoon across town to that very same club called Baker's Bar. It was a good walk, and Miss C. complained endlessly about the distance. Now and then, H. Grouse took a rest, put his sax case down on the pavement and pulled his long, shabby overcoat (with the 'Make our Planet Great Again' button) into his body like he was giving himself a hug. I couldn't help but notice how the doomed driftwood leg complied with his movement most of the time, only to stray off course as if it had been caught in a rogue current or distracted by the sound of a screaming ambulance or a police car speeding by. Then H. Grouse would have to stop walking to rearrange his leg like you would attempt to rearrange a dishevelled child with a snotty nose. I admit to you now that I enjoyed what I was doing. It seemed forbidden and adventurous because I would never have considered being in that part of the city before. Once I thought Grouse spotted me, but if he had, he never let on. When we reached Baker's Bar, I am certain he turned to wave at me before he disappeared into the dark bowels of the building. I think I waved back. I like to think I did. But most likely, if he had, I would have looked away, disgusted at the behaviour Miss C. and I were exhibiting by reducing ourselves to this type of scum. For following H. Grouse across an off-limits neighbourhood to a bar called Baker's, where God knows what kind of decrepit rooms lay within. Really, how could you?, we both asked of each other as Miss C., bright red in the face and practically out of breath, begged me to hail a taxi cab to take us both home.

Now See What You've Done

I dreamt I was sitting at the kitchen table and the child across from me was asking in a loud, demanding voice why I had hung the plates on the wall and how come I could be so trusting about the plates on the wall and did I not know that they were going to fall down, and then as soon as he said that, the plates fell off the wall one by one and crashed into smithereens all over the floor, and while he was saying this to me he began to laugh and in a jeering fashion said, 'Now see what you've done,' while pointing to the wall where the plates used to be, and I saw how the white wall was now covered in solid black stains where the plates used to be, and round black circles and oval circles and big and small circles glared back at me like angry raccoon eyes, and then the child stood up, shook his angelic blond head at me in disgust and walked away out of the room leaving me behind to pick up the pieces.

A Music Lesson in the Afternoon

The following note appeared on the kitchen counter. It was
from Herbert Grouse:

'Could you please attend to the sink in my room:

it appears to be clogged?

Thank you – H.G.'

'Knockety knock, Mr G.

It's me and (to myself) Miss C.'

'C-come i-in' said H.G.

Jauntily in through the door we go. Room is presentable with
nothing amiss. Been a good boy, I see H.G.

'What's up, H.G.?' says Miss C.

'Cloggedy sink.'

'Righty oh, let me see'.

Of course it didn't happen that way. I stood momentarily out
in the hallway. To be honest, I was nervous to be there and
considered turning away. When I got up the courage to knock,

Herbert Grouse opened it without delay and stood aside to allow me to enter. The room smelled of sage and lemons and sheets of paper covered in fresh squiggles of music. It was a smell I didn't expect to smell in his room. Herbert Grouse's saxophone lay on the bed, elegant and seductive like an abandoned lover lying patiently awaiting H.G.'s attention, or it very well could have been a great freshly polished ampersand placed on its side.

Herbert Grouse wore a pullover the colour of oatmeal and a baggy pair of dark chocolate corduroy trousers well worn at the knees. It unsettled me that his unshaven face had me thinking that I would have liked to feel the soft sprout of bristly wheat grass, allow it to tickle my skin. So what I wanted to say to Herbert Grouse that day was:

Hello.

Herbert Grouse.

How.

Are.

You?

I.

Am.

Resisting.

The.

Urge.

To.

Touch.

You.

Right now.

No. But I didn't say that even though that's what Miss C. suggested I say. Instead, using my formal landlady voice, I said, 'I brought the liquid for the clogged sink,' and put it down carefully on the table. Then I couldn't believe I was telling him how I thought the saxophone to be most alluring while I reached down to touch the deep blue velvet lining of the open case. It reminded me of the spreading out on the summer-grass days when nothing mattered, only to be looking up at the cloud-free-sky days, I said. Then Herbert Grouse picked up the instrument so gently that it could have been a sleeping child that needed to be carried to its cot and said to me, ever so softly, as if reciting a poem for my ears only,

Y-yes, he said, and y-you are n-not ex-expecting me to s-say this b-but would y-you like to t-try it? So:

1. I had to stand up straight like I was back in school in PE class.
2. I had to put the saxophone strap around my neck.
3. I had to fasten the strap to the saxophone.

4. I had to say that I found the saxophone strangely heavy and alien in my hands.
5. He had to stand behind me.
6. He had to stand behind me and guide my fingers to rest on the keys.
7. He had to say, now relax.
8. I had to put the mouthpiece into my mouth.
9. He had to say, yes, blow, blow from the deepest part inside of you.
10. I had to blow. I blew and felt his breath fall like a never-ending kiss warm on the nape of my neck.
11. I had to hear the sound emerge as a raw, croaking, pleading sound. Of someone-calling-out-in-the-midnight-darkness sound. Of the-longest-and-loneliest-night sound. And of someone-who-was-totally-exhausted-from-not-being-heard sound and a not-being-seen sound. Of someone who, close to giving up, somehow still managed a last-gasp attempt at salvation by reaching down inside herself and blowing hard, so damn hard her entire body ached.

I Might Have. I Might Have. I Might Have.

I might have followed Herbert Grouse one more time. I knew he was headed to Baker's Bar. His routine was such that on Wednesday and Thursday afternoons, he left his room early to cover the two-plus mile journey carrying with him his beautiful saxophone (which is really like an ampersand turned on its side). I might have been wishing for him to see me this time. I might have even dared to hurry and catch up with him, reached out to touch him on the shoulder and say, hey, H.G., do you mind if I walk alongside you? I might have been wondering what'd gotten into me, to be walking with this man across the dirty footpaths and crowded crosswalks in this city full of cobblestoned cul-de-sacs and screaming sirens. I might have been telling him things I never told anyone before apart from Miss C. He might have been listening intently. He might have been, now and then, saying to me, 'I-I u-under-s-stand, I s-see, y-yes'. I might have been stopping and resting with him while the unending throng of people passed us by, not once considering our connection. I might have been saying something about the rooms, the emptiness, the years, the solitude, the silence, the voices, the waiting, and the longing for something else. I might have been listening to him tell me how he knew about me, how it hadn't taken him long to figure me out. I might have gotten to Baker's Bar with him and found myself in a green baize room where velvet burgundy drapes, long and luxurious, hung in the windows to numb the sounds from the city street. I might have talked all that afternoon to H.G. as he cradled his saxophone on his lap, listening intently, clasping and unclasping his hands, his graceful hands like a prayer of sorts opening themselves up to me and I, in turn, beginning to try to unravel some of the knotted wool in my mind, so that his hands were to become a kind of microphone I spoke into allowing the pages of the rooms to finally appear in a somewhat manageable order, like chapters in a book, each one making sense of what previously had been laid out.

Happy Days

I decided to confront him once and for all. To tell him how all along I knew about the woman who smelled like spring flowers. I really had no choice in the matter. It was no longer possible to keep the knowledge within me. Miss C. adamantly agreed and actually insisted I broach the matter, saying that it was the right time to approach him in as much of a civilized and mature fashion as I could possibly muster. She insisted I have it out with him because 'you cannot, simply cannot go on like this'. Spit it all out, she said.

But spit-it-out time wasn't as easy as it sounds because first I had to watch him from across the top of the cereal box plonked in the middle of the kitchen table. He was scattering blueberries and flaxseed into the bowl because that's what good boys eat. It annoyed me that he was reading the slogan of the cereal box like he could have been reading a bestselling novel:

'What do you say,

eat this now to be okay

for you'll never go astray with Happy Day'

I was trying to formulate a strategy:

1. What happened to the woman who smelled like spring flowers? I know about the woman who smelled like spring flowers. No. I'm just curious about that client of yours who smelled like spring flowers. How is she? Yes.

So I allowed the words – I'm just curious about that client of yours who smelled like spring flowers, how is she? – to slowly crawl out of my mouth and rise up and over the Happy Day cereal box to land right before him.

Oh yes, he said, slurping the milk, I do. Why do you ask?

Just curious, I said, how is she doing these days?

She died, he said, spooning up the dregs of the extra low-fat double-pressed almond milk swirled into extra crunchy spoonfuls of Happy Day cereal tossed in agave syrup. She died four months ago, left behind a devoted husband and two kids. Sad, he said, very sad, he said. And then I was or Miss C. was or we both were throwing my cereal spoon in his direction where it hit him on the left cheek, and his face turned bright red. He looked confused and angry and hurt, and all the time, Miss C. was snickering and jabbing me in the back, saying, 'Now look what you've done, you big fool,' as the room I never thought possible, the room we so often jokingly hinted at began to seem a reality. Yes, that room, carefully omitted until then, until the spoon hit his cheek, until the crunchy kernels spilled all over the tabletop, until the coffee from our cups ran into streams that trickled onto the floor, and until the table-cloth slid down too like the final curtain in a stage play where the woman laughs hysterically and uncontrollably as the man pleads with her to stop, to calm down, saying all is okay, to please relax, it was okay, hush now. Was he touching me then? Was he smoothing my hair like a disillusioned runaway who had come home? Was he looking concerned? Was he putting me to bed, careful to tuck me in? Was he standing by the bedside until he believed I slept? Was he leaving the room? Quietly closing the door to go downstairs to call a colleague to arrange something for me? Was I lying in bed aware of all of this but still observing it as from a distance floating above myself and wondering, is that me or you, Miss C.? Was I asking Miss C. is that how you behave when I'm not looking, or was she asking me? And the room, a good host for the pain and loneliness, extended its arms out to me, ready to accept and embrace and absolve me from all wrongs so that I could lie and wait for the pain to subside within walls, quietly weeping with relief. I could hear them sob somewhat self-consciously, emitting muffled stutters and hiccups of regret that sounded like tiny childlike voices calling out Mother, Daddy, don't say that and then innocent laughter, as wispy and transient as the turning of pages in a well-worn nursery rhyme book whilst humming a familiar tune, only this time with different words:

There was a mad woman who lived in a room

and wondered some days if it could be a tomb

so she opened the windows

to climb on the sill

and thought about flying away up the hill.

Now Is This the Mad Room?

Before everything changed I wanted the sky to be permanently blue and full of light, wispy clouds. But when I reached out I only felt the rain on my hand, and I remember asking of no one in particular, where did the sunlight go? Someone confidently replied, 'There's a high pressure way out over the Atlantic and supposedly heading our way. You'll have sun tomorrow afternoon. The weather crowd usually get it right.' I did not look to the voice. Instead, upon closing the window, I sank back down into the blue velvet chair I favoured. A group in the corner of the room had started up a game of cards, and I heard someone cough hard and blow his nose. I especially liked the view from my place by the window and how the crafty fog stole in off the shore to cast itself like a net curtain over the building and the jagged cluster of cypress trees on the hills behind. Still, I missed the sunlight and longed for the next day when I could sit again in the garden to watch cars go by or hear a distant jet overhead and count the vapour trails before they dissipated. How long had I been there? When I asked, I got only mumbled replies from voices transmitting a garbled mishmash of information. Don't you know, they asked. Come on now, think. What kind of a question is that? La, la, la. Was I mad? If so, I don't know when I got mad. I do remember thinking I'd had enough. I remember wishing I could stay in bed all day and not have to rise. I remember feeling cold and not wanting to be warm. I remember my body being permanently asleep like a long and heavy piece of clay. Grey lumpy clay.

The Foggy Rooms

I fought them. I did. I thought I might not have a good chance of winning, but at the very least I had to try. I was easily outnumbered. There was no doubting that. I kept thinking about the condition in human behaviour where people prefer to move in packs, like herds of animals. Well that's what they did. They moved like an arrogant herd of elephants crossing the plains of Africa slowly but surely. No rush, biding their time. We'll get there. We'll get you, is what they were really saying. I remember repeating that old adage 'birds of a feather stick together', aware that I was certainly not one of the birds. Well, Miss C. said she had figured it all out, reminding me not to forget how they were the ones with the problem and not us. Still, I was fragile. Fragile isn't the right word. I was at the very last part of myself, the bottom half inch of existence. Mornings on waking and looking out the window, I'd blindly convince myself that I could fly before I realised my wings had been clipped. To make matters worse, the others stood around me laughing and whispering about my pointless expectations. They were so self-assured, banded together like super glue, never to become undone. When he came to visit me in that place where the fog rarely lifted, I heard him before I saw him by the way the gravelled driveway crunched beneath the car tyres, followed quickly by the smooth, reliable thud of the car door closing before he made tentative steps to the doorbell at the entrance. Often times I secretly observed him walking along the corridor. He appeared more serious than usual, worried and distracted and once, I wanted to reach out to him and say how I craved to be better. I wanted to force myself to recall the certain and special something we had before a long time before, but I could not, so I pretended when I saw him that I was at ease and feeling what he maybe tried to recall too.

I knew though, he could easily see through to the shadows playing catch in my mind, the lonely stubborn shadows in the corners of those blasted rooms waiting for an opportunity to pounce and ridicule any feeble attempts I might be entertaining about how we could retrieve the beginning once more, despite the members of the herd relishing how the thick gunk that clung to my very being kept me at bay at all times.

Adieu Miss C.

A day not long but long enough after the Happy Day cereal day was the day when Miss C. and I broke up. It wasn't something I had ever thought possible, but now, in retrospect, I see how inevitable it really was. The truth is she was getting on my nerves, constantly agitating me with her sarcastic comments and suspicious views and bickering with the world. And so, on that particular day, as I lay in the silent place of the foggy rooms thinking about opening the window and once and for all leaving her and the rooms behind, I saw to my dismay that she had beaten me to it. I saw how she had climbed down off the bed and removed her nightgown to let it slither quickly to the floor. I saw her unlatch the window and stand on the sill for about a minute until she grew increasingly smaller, so by the time she stepped forward, a sudden gust of wind was able to pick her up and carry her away like a fragile white feather drifting north into the cold night air. I remember lying back down on the bed feeling strangely empty as if something I'd never known but was so heavy inside of me was suddenly exorcised like an invisible tumour or how those participants on My Six Hundred Pound Life programmes on T.V., who, after months of dieting and exercise, finally get up out of bed to venture outdoors into their gardens for the first time in years where you see them standing before the flower beds looking nervous because they had forgotten what a black-eyed Susan or a dahlia looks like in September sunlight, all smiling and yellow and bright. Well, it's true, I felt a little bit like that too, like I didn't know what to do with myself, like someone had taken away a crutch that I'd depended on all of my life and left with no option but to fend for myself, I sat up and pulled back the sheets to take in the room. I saw, to my amazement, how the room was simply a room with four walls, one bed, a sink, a window, a rubbish bin, a door. And then I looked in the mirror only to realise that I did not recognise the person looking back at me.

The Beginning of the Ending

After the storm finally died and blew northward, the sun broke through to warm and regenerate the long-neglected parts of my being. I wanted nothing more than fresh air as I was able to picture the rooms demolished after a swift and stealthy digger stole in and destroyed them in my absence. It was then that I dreamed of living in a big open field, boundary-free, ruled only by the constant line of sea to the south and a sylvan glade to the north, and right in the middle of the lush green field, I would stand knocking on the doorway to his soul before lying beneath the roof of his body where we could fold back into each other once more, safe and secure within our very own pliable walls.

Before the Beginning

Door key slips into waiting keyhole, and post box lid flaps twice to welcome me back to the home of the still rooms with doors closed shut tight that will never speak to me again because they've been told to shut up, warned by the boss not to dare utter another word or else there will be trouble.

And I am home with him in the kitchen where he brews tea, happy to be moving timidly from sink to stove, in a body that oddly appears new and supple to me. His frown-free face invites me to come back to him. There are fresh mint leaves in blue tea cups set on the small table in the sun-dappled room overlooking the garden where we could be people seeing each other, with freshly installed eyes, for the very first time. There we sit as we wait for evening to claim us before we need to consider adjusting ourselves.

He tells me Herbert Grouse has moved on. I am pleased to hear that. He received an alternative offer, he said, back in the old city where he had come from. He left without any fuss, just as he had come.

Then soon after that, the days blend into one another. A series of easy blends like smooth yoghurt swished with puréed fruit enabling me to mindfully digest each day until it is time for me to re-enter the rooms. There are, I admit, moments when Miss C. comes to mind, and I wonder why she hasn't, as futile as it might seem, accosted me to bargain for her return. It's as if everything has been one eternal dream, so much so that I sometimes wonder if I too had conjured up Herbert Grouse, but no, there I am, tentatively opening the door to his room to discover how the fusty air within reminds me of hotel rooms in lonely, dormant seaside resorts midwinter. Nothing more than that. I do consider turning away then. It seems only right to close the door for good until I see a small box has been left on the bed.

You see, this is the part I have been waiting for, for so long. Long since I was a young woman and mother lying in the cold light of morning, wondering how to proceed. Long since I stood at the kitchen sink and watched the days pass by outside the window without finding any sign of where to begin. Long since each room, decorated and lavished upon, only came to disappoint. Now I know this to be the very last bit of reaching the end to allow the proper beginning to begin. It is why I have written thus far.

And so to start over I must first place the slender silver pen he left for me into my hand and with a quiet prayer of gratitude to all that has gone before.

I begin.

ACKNOWLEDGEMENTS

My sincere thanks to David Borrowdale at Reflex Press for believing in *Quotidian*. Thank you to all the rooms and the people within them who have inspired this book. Thank you to my confidante Will and to my three wonderful sons, Kyle, Drew and Zane for being there when the words were not.

REFLEX PRESS

Reflex Press is an independent publisher based in Abingdon, Oxfordshire, committed to publishing bold and innovative books by emerging authors from across the UK and beyond.

Since our inception in 2018, we have published award-winning short story collections, flash fiction anthologies, and novella-length fiction.

www.reflex.press
@reflexfiction

Made in the USA
Coppell, TX
03 November 2023

23766501R00111